The Hemp Miracle

The Hemp Miracle

How One Miraculous Plant is Healing the Planet and Its People

Second Edition

Carol Merlo M.Ed.

MM MPowered Press

Contents

Preface to the Second Edition

The road to acceptance and the significant research that has been done in the past two years since I first wrote *The Hemp Miracle* has been significant. Not only has the US legislature passed the Farm Bill of 2018, thereby deregulating hemp and allowing its cultivation and production, the processing methods and research that has gone into the health benefits of the components of hemp have brought hemp into the awareness of the public in a large way.

Because so much has changed, I felt it was important to update this book and provide my readers with current information that will further facilitate the cultivation and use of hemp and hemp products in the US and across the world.

In this edition, I have expanded the information about terpenes and processing methods so that you can make more informed decisions about which products to purchase. Further, I have provided more up to date information on the deregulation and uses of industrial hemp so that you can be a more powerful advocate of its use.

While we have come a long way since 2017, we must be diligent in spreading the news about hemp. We have the potential to alleviate climate issues, housing, and shelter concerns, as well as providing a renewable food source for those who are currently undernourished in the world. We can also improve the health and emotional wellbeing of millions of people by understanding the value of hemp as a dietary supplement.

Please enjoy this new edition and spread the word about the Hemp Miracle!

Introduction

I want to introduce you to a plant that I have found to be miraculous; a plant that is so beneficial that every person needs to know about it, yet knowledge about its benefits and value have been stigmatized, feared, and suppressed for the last one hundred years. The plant is hemp. You might assume, like I did, that hemp is marijuana. You may or may not be an advocate or user, but this book is not about marijuana or even medical marijuana. This is a book about the value of hemp—a plant that is like marijuana but doesn't get you high and has completely different properties and uses.

I want you to discover these miraculous properties and so will arm you with facts—facts that may surprise, anger, and, hopefully, inspire you to take action to join me in becoming an advocate of hemp. Facts can overcome prejudice and ignorance. Facts can present a case that builds hope and a sense of possibility.

This book reflects my journey through the history and uses of hemp for healing the planet and its people. In the beginning, I was just as ignorant as you might be now. I have been familiar with marijuana since I was a teenager in the late sixties but didn't know anything about hemp until recently. I sure didn't know the difference between pot and hemp. Back then, smoking marijuana was a phenomenon. It was part of a social revolution grounded in a belief that the rigid establishment of the depression era generation had no idea what was good for humanity and was destroying the planet, not to mention killing our young people in a war that did not pose a threat to our way of life. Timothy Leary encouraged us to "Tune In, Turn On, and Drop Out"—to reject the dictates of society and experience the deeper truths that transcended cultural mores, for that was the path to peace and freedom.

Where I lived in Los Angeles, possession of marijuana was a felony. The rules were so rigid about this plant you could smoke that it was plain ridiculous to us. We believed that pot wasn't as damaging or as dangerous as alcohol, yet possession of any amount of it carried greater penalties. It had the onus of being a "Gateway Drug." The prevailing assumption was that if kids smoked pot, they would go on to using heroin and become a burden on society. For me, as for many others, that was a clear example of the contrast between logic and dogma that our generation was fighting.

So, why on earth was an entire generation so willing to smoke marijuana, despite the potential consequences? According to the *Gallup organization*, the earliest survey data on marijuana use in the U.S. was in the spring of 1967. This was just prior to the "Summer of Love" in San Francisco. The nationally-based telephone poll of college students found that 5% had used it at least once in their lifetime. In 1969, it jumped to 22%. In the fall of 1970, 43% of college students reported trying marijuana, and by 1971, over half (51%) of the nation's college students reported having tried it. In this brief four years, use of marijuana went from 5% to 51% among young people. There was a disconnect between obedience to the law and the pursuit of pleasure led by the baby boom generation that had outcomes we are seeing in the 21st century. Think about that. Four years to transform a culture.

My use of marijuana dwindled pretty quickly after high school. While I did smoke it--mostly to fit in--I didn't like the feeling of being stoned and so had moved on to meditation as a spiritual practice by the time I was 20. I never lost my social conscience, though, and always believed that incarcerating people for the use or sale of

4

marijuana was a damaging and costly practice for our society. I wasn't alone.

Over the years, I lost touch with anyone who smoked marijuana. I was busy surviving in the world and didn't have time to pay attention to recreational 'drugs.' But then, a few years ago, I started learning about *medical marijuana* and all the benefits it had for people with cancer. I have been studying dietary supplements for over twenty years and so I am always on the lookout for something natural that works instead of invasive and toxic medications. I was intrigued, to say the least. I watched as Colorado and California legalized recreational marijuana, followed by other states. I watched economies boom where marijuana was legalized. I decided that if I ever got cancer, I would move to a state that allowed it. But that was the extent of my knowledge about the subject.

Then I Discovered CBD-Rich Hemp Oil

A few years ago, I learned about CBD-rich hemp oil and the benefits it has for people with pain. I have some back pain from a bad disc and so I was excited about the possibilities of trying it. I didn't know anything about how CBD-rich hemp oil was created but I heard that it worked. I started doing research on it and discovered that it comes from hemp, which is cannabis (I thought that was just pot) but it is legally available for sale in every state and has no psychoactive properties. These facts were confusing, to say the least, since I knew that marijuana was illegal in my state. I figured that, since hemp is pot, they must extract the THC out of it to make hemp oil. So, my thinking was just as ignorant about this as some of our top legislators who might think hemp is pot and pot is a threat to our society.

By this time, I had started hearing from some friends about it. One friend with fibromyalgia told me she bought some online and took it for her pain. She was now doing yoga and feeling great. Then I heard from another friend who suffers with severe pain from fibromyalgia who is now pain free. It usually takes hearing from two different people before I am willing to try something. I thought, "what if it can do that for me?" I ordered some from a reputable manufacturer that came in a dropper bottle.

I put a dropper full under my tongue and within a few minutes I had a sensation like nothing else I had ever experienced! Now, as I said, I meditate and am very sensitive to my emotional, cognitive, and physical states. I can quickly tell how food and nutrients affect me. The closest I can come to describing the sensation I felt was a wave of deep relief that came over me. I wasn't stoned or high. Instead, it felt like I was finally getting something I had been starving for my entire life! That day, some of the stressors I had been feeling overwhelmed by suddenly seemed to be like child's play. I had a level of calm and grace at my core. The next day, the same thing happened. I was on the phone with a friend and felt like I was lifted out of the molasses-like 'bulldozing through life' method I had been operating out of into a state of confidence and ease.

I went online and bought five bottles right then and there! I decided that I never wanted to run out of this stuff. I was so amazed by my experience that I started doing research to discover what this was and why it had taken me so long to discover it. I looked at sites about the medical benefits of CBD. I looked for doses. I looked at the companies that sell CBD-rich hemp oil. I even researched the science and history. After all, I was a fan! At the time, I didn't realize I would become an advocate, too.

Now, in full disclosure, that feeling of a rush of satiety I got in the beginning did not increase with more doses during the day or even every day. I appear to have leveled off when my body got what it needed. At this point, if I go two days without it, I will have that sensation again.

6

So, what I know is that my maintenance level is 25 mg per day, unless I have unusual stressors to deal with.

What I also know is that *your experience may not be like mine.* You may need 1 mg a day. You may need to take it two to four times a day. I don't know what you will need but I do know, after having done this research, is that you DO need it. This is why:

The Endocannabinoid System

It turns out that the body has a system similar to the immune, cardiovascular, or endocrine systems called the *endocannabinoid system*, or ECS. The ECS influences your hormones and immune cells, and acts like a regulator to create balance in the body and mind. It modulates the function of neurotransmitters to promote a sense of relaxation, joy, focus, and inspiration. This system relies on specific nutrients, called *cannabinoids*, to function properly. The body can make its own cannabinoids, but it can also be deficient in them. Just like the lack of any nutrient can facilitate the breakdown of one's health, the lack of cannabinoids can cause a breakdown in the ECS.

Cannabis is the primary natural source of these special nutrients. While they are found in both hemp and marijuana, I am focusing only on hemp in this book. Hemp-based cannabidiol nutritional supplement products can supply the body with the nutrients it needs to restore and maintain good health and emotional balance. While there is a lot of research still needed on the possible causes of endocannabinoid deficiency and its ramifications, I believe that it is affecting millions of people and all that is needed for them to resolve health issues that are plaguing them is education.

CBD-rich hemp oil is just one of the uses for this miraculous hemp plant. My research showed me that for centuries, the entire hemp plant has been used as a food, for clothing, paper, textiles, and can be used for biodegradable plastics, construction materials, and even as a clean fuel source. Hemp is healthy for the planet and its people in so many ways that it boggles the mind.

The Challenge

So now, here's the kicker. Despite it being so useful and even though it is completely different from marijuana, there are legal hurdles to overcome before we will see hemp as a viable commercial product in the US, while many other countries in the world have gotten on the hemp band wagon and are making it into an economically viable resource.

My purpose in writing this book is to share the facts about hemp and its benefits and to enlighten anyone who is ready for the truth. I have endeavored to provide you with the most current and accurate information I have found in books and online. I have gone to the actual source documents to eliminate hyperbole and hype. The truth about hemp is so good, there is no reason to create conspiracy theories about it.

The simple truth is that hemp is not pot. Hemp is a safe, miraculous plant with amazing life-giving health benefits that can also be used for over 25,000 clean, green industrial products. The information I am providing you is meant to educate and to encourage you to learn more and become an advocate for hemp cultivation in the US.

PART ONE

How Hemp Became
Confused with Marijuana

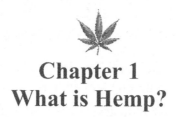

Chapter 1
What is Hemp?

The words cannabis, hemp, and marijuana are often confused with one another. Any of these words can conjure up images of hippies smoking joints and craving carbs. Yet, I recently discovered that anyone going to a health food store can purchase hemp seeds, hemp protein, hemp cooking oil, skin care products, and even dietary supplements made from hemp oil. There are also other uses for hemp that are not found in the health food store. People rarely think of hemp in terms of plant-based plastics, building materials, durable paper, or military grade fabric. Yet, the hemp plant provides all of these products in a clean, planet-friendly manner.

Now, at the beginning of this journey, I figured that CBD-rich hemp oil came from marijuana and that the THC had been somehow extracted from the cannabis. Nothing could be further from the truth. The reason for the all this confusion is that cannabis is the name of the species the plant that has been used for thousands of years for everything from building materials to spiritual awakening rituals.

So, what's the difference, then? Let's look at it from a scientific viewpoint. According to the *ITIS Taxonomy Report*, there are three *subspecies* of cannabis sativa:

1). C. sativa sativa,

2). C. sativa indica,

3). C. sativa ruderalis.

I had never heard of ruderalis and, as far as I know, no one smokes that! But people do smoke indica and sativa. Well, that was interesting, but it didn't tell me where CBD came from. More digging led me to discover that, irrespective of subspecies, cannabis plants contain at least 480 natural components, 111 of which are called *cannabinoids*. Cannabinoids are the *active compounds* in the plant. Now I was getting somewhere.

It turns out that industrial hemp—the kind that CBD-rich hemp oil comes from—*is the exact same plant as marijuana*. So, the subspecies evolved as humans began to cultivate it for different properties. The difference between the two plants (marijuana and hemp) is in the breeding, climate, and environmental conditions it has been exposed to over generations.

I like to compare hemp and marijuana with the races of humanity. All humans are homo sapiens *sapiens*. (*I know it seems weird to repeat the name of the species as the subspecies, but I guess they ran out of cool names*). Races of humans are different, though. Asians typically have straight black hair, while Africans have curly black hair and Northern Europeans typically have very blond or red hair. Yet, despite our physical differences, we are all homo sapiens *sapiens*. You can see how this plays out in the dog world, too. A Great Dane is the same subspecies as a Chihuahua. So, while hemp and marijuana are quite different from one another, they are the same subspecies of cannabis sativa.

What is the Difference Between Hemp and Marijuana?

There are distinct differences between marijuana and hemp. The term *'hemp'* typically refers to the industrial/commercial use of the cannabis stalk and seed used for textiles, foods, papers, body care products, detergents, plastics and building materials. The term *marijuana* refers to the medicinal, recreational, or spiritual use resulting from smoking or eating cannabis flowers or leaf resin.

The main difference between the two is the ratio of CBD to THC. If you are new to this conversation, you need to know that hemp has almost no THC, which is the psychoactive component in marijuana. The international definition of hemp is *cannabis sativa that contains 0.3 percent or less THC. (That's three tenths of one percent— virtually none!)*

The leaves of industrial hemp and marijuana look the same but that is where the comparison ends. In fact, marijuana growers avoid cross pollination with hemp at all costs. If hemp pollinates any marijuana that is nearby, the resulting plant will always be lower-THC marijuana instead of higher-THC hemp.

So, by now I think you have an inkling of why hemp was criminalized along with marijuana. It has been lumped into the same category as marijuana and has been stigmatized in the United States and most parts of the world for the last 80-100 years. However, all of that is changing. Over 30 countries are now growing hemp for dietary supplement, medical, and industrial uses and people are waking up to the Hemp Miracle.

The value of hemp and its uses are becoming more popular and it is up to us to help the world become educated about it. Even today, some states in the US have ridiculously prohibitive regulations against the possession of hemp because of this confusion.

Characteristics of Hemp

- Cultivated and farmed outdoors and grows to become 6-15 feet in 3-4 months
- Needs few to no pesticides because grows quickly and blocks weeds

- Is harvested for its fiber, seeds, seed meal, and oil
- Has higher concentrations of cannabidiol (CBD) and strict limits on THC content to less than 0.3%
- Primarily male and lacks budding flowers
- Oils are used for healing purposes, are legal, and are regulated by the US Department of Agriculture

Characteristics of Marijuana

- Best cultivated indoors under controlled conditions and grows 2-5 feet
- Bushy
- Is harvested for recreational and medicinal use
- Contains .4%-20% THC
- Female

Chapter 2
The History of Hemp

Did marijuana suddenly show up in the back rooms of jazz clubs to be smoked by hip and cool musicians? Not exactly. In fact, cannabis is probably one of the world's oldest domesticated crops. There is a lot of evidence to show that throughout history, humans have grown different varieties of cannabis for either industrial or medicinal uses.

As I looked through the information online and in books on the history of hemp, I found that most of the information was consistent. One particularly detailed reference I found is from www.advancedholistichealth.org. I am giving you a selection from a long list of events in the history of hemp and encourage you to sit down with a nice cup of tea and enjoy this history lesson.

The archaeological record shows that hemp fibers were used for making cloth and other textiles such as baskets and rope, and ancient writings refer to its use. I learned that there was evidence of hemp cord in pottery in Asia as early as 8,000 BC, where Taiwan exists today. That is 10,000 years ago, which makes it one of the earliest examples of human agriculture and the start of the transition from us being a hunter-gatherer society to an agrarian society. **Imagine how important hemp must have been to those early people if it was the reason they decided to stay in one place?**

One possible reason for its cultivation is its value as medicine. For example, hemp appears to have been grown in China for over 4500 years, where it was used for its medicinal benefits. Traditional Chinese medicine uses herbs to strengthen the body and prevent illness rather than to fight illnesses after they have appeared. In the ancient writings, hemp is considered to be an herb and it appears to have been one of the primary and most important among the ancient Chinese.

In neighboring India, Ayurveda is the traditional medical practice. It promotes maintaining health through achieving balance between mind, body, and spirit. Ayurveda uses herbs and foods to maintain body balance. Cannabis was important in this culture—not only for medical purposes—but also for religious and spiritual practices. It is mentioned in the Hindu sacred text Atharvaveda (Science of Charms) as "Sacred Grass", as far back as 2000 BC, as one of the five sacred plants of India, and was used medicinally and ritually as an offering to the god Shiva. They called it *bhang* (do you think that has any relevance to the word bong?) It was regarded as a source of happiness. Medicinally, Indians blended hemp milk and spices into a drink that was used to aid digestion, decrease pain, relieve fever, and treat dysentery.

Hemp was introduced into Northern Europe by Persian nomads around 500 BC. An urn that contained cannabis leaves and seeds was found near Berlin and dated to that time. In Europe, hemp fibers were popular and widely used among the Germans, the Franks, and the Vikings around 600 AD.

There is evidence of the Persians adopting the Chinese process of making hemp paper in 700 AD, where it spread to Africa. By 850 AD, the first hemp paper mill was built in Egypt.

The use of hemp for cloth, paper, medicine, and rope was commonplace for the next one thousand years!

Hemp continued to be grown as a crop around the world. In 1533, King Henry VIII fined farmers if they didn't raise hemp for industrial use. Queen Elizabeth I is reported to have used it for menstrual cramps. In 1564, King Philip of Spain followed England's lead and ordered cannabis to be grown throughout his empire, which extended from modern-day Argentina to Oregon, and so brought it to the new world.

I imagine that the English brought hemp with them from England, because it was cultivated in the American colonies as the first settlers arrived. In 1619, Virginia made hemp cultivation mandatory. Hemp was used as currency from the mid 1600's.

By the 18th century, hemp cultivation was a common practice, here. George Washington pushed for the growth of hemp and even grew it himself as a cash crop for rope and fabric. In 1791, he encouraged domestic hemp industries and Thomas Jefferson urged farmers to replace tobacco with hemp, calling hemp a 'necessity'. The Declaration of Independence was drafted on hemp paper before the final document was written on parchment.

Cannabis was added to the U.S. Pharmacopoeia in 1850. During the 1800's, hemp oil was prescribed as a medicine for everything from cramps, headache, digestive problems, vomiting, and insomnia, to chronic seizures.

How Cannabis Became Prohibited

There are a lot of conspiracy theories about why hemp was banished from the United States. I have attempted here to separate fact from fiction, yet I know that none of us knows what might have occurred between powerful and rich influencers and the legal prohibitions that took place in the early part of the twentieth century. I found a fascinating and thorough article called *The History of the Marihuana*

Tax Act of 1937. It cleared up for me any misconceptions about the collusion on the part of a few individuals to outlaw hemp. Now, I truly believe that hemp was poorly differentiated from marijuana and so they threw the baby out with the bath water, but I am open to other ideas on this.

According to that article, "The anti-marihuana law of 1937 was largely the federal government's response to political pressure from enforcement agencies and other alarmed groups who feared the use and spread of marihuana by "Mexicans." Recent evidence also suggests that the Federal Bureau of Narcotics resisted the enforcement burden of the anti-marihuana law until mounting pressure on the Treasury Department led to a departmental decision, probably in 1935, to appease this fear, mostly in the Southwest and West, by federal legislation."

Let's walk through the early twentieth century and see what happened to get us to that place.

By the mid-19th century, cotton was America's leading export, due to the invention of the cotton gin, which made it easy to separate the seed and husk from the cotton fiber. An equivalent hemp processing machine had not been invented, so slaves were the only cost-effective way to separate the hemp fiber from the pulpy core that was used to make cloth. When slavery ended, it was cheaper to make cloth from cotton than to make it from hemp.

At the same time cotton became king, paper makers had found an economical way to convert trees to pulp to make paper. It was cheaper to pay laborers to chop down trees than to process hemp. The use of wood to make pulp for paper began when a machine was invented to create pulp in the 1840's and, by 1900, *sulfite* pulping had become the dominant means of producing wood pulp because it could process a wide variety of types of wood and produce stronger fibers. That, along with the abundance of soft and hardwood trees in the continental US, made paper production from wood the most economically viable method for producing paper, and so hemp paper manufacturing was discontinued. However, hemp was still being used for rope, but the US started importing it from Manila instead of growing it here.

With less industrial use, all cannabis was seen for its medical properties only instead of differentiating the two. By the turn of the century, the Federal government assumed responsibility for legislative control of medicine, and cannabis became a target. The earliest example of this is the *Pure Food and Drug Act of 1906,* which required that any quantity of cannabis, as well as several other so-called "dangerous substances", be clearly marked on the labels of any drug or food sold to the public.

While there was legislation in 1914 to further prohibit cocaine and opiates, cannabis was not yet included. At the time, the pharmaceutical industry did not see any reason why cannabis should be so severely restricted in its use and sale. Not even the reformers in the pre-World War I hearings and debates over a federal anti-narcotic act claimed that it was a problem of any major significance in the United States.

The Beginning of the Fear of Marijuana

It appears that the fear of marijuana wasn't prevalent in the culture until an influx of Mexican immigration during the 1920's occurred from Louisiana to California and up to Colorado and Utah. Mexicans were encouraged to come here because they were seen as cheap farm laborers. They brought with them the term marijuana and its culture. So, while hemp was still being produced for rope and cloth, the intoxicating aspects of it were not in the forefront until this time.

Even though the US had welcomed them as a source of cheap labor, their cultural differences inspired fear in the states where they were living, so the perception of Mexicans was that they were criminals who smoked this 'marijuana.' During the mid-1920's a couple of horrible crimes were attributed to Mexicans who used marijuana, and that was enough to trigger a media blitz of 'yellow journalism' in the Hearst newspapers that raged in the late 1920's and 1930's. Then, as now, people tend to believe what they read—whether it's in a newspaper or in Social Media. This flood of media did its job to create a wave of terror about the use of marijuana.

This wave of terror created pressure to amend the federal law which controlled similar substances, resulting in the *Harrison Narcotic Act*, which did not include marijuana despite attempts to do so. However, it did lead to the Marijuana Tax Act of 1937.

The US Treasury needed the cooperation of the State Department to push through the Marijuana Tax Act. So, the State Department tentatively agreed to its approval with the caveat that *"We must satisfy the canary bird seed trade, and the Sherwin Williams Paint Company which uses hemp seed oil for drying purposes. We are now working with the Department of Commerce in finding substitutes for the legitimate trade, and after that is accomplished, the path will be cleared for the treaties and for federal law."*

What this means to me is that they understood the difference between hemp and marijuana but could not see a way to criminalize one without the other.

The *Marihuana Tax Act of 1937* levied a $100-an-ounce tax on cannabis for medicinal and non-medical use, despite the fact that the American Medical Association (AMA) opposed the act because physicians were required to pay a special tax when they prescribed it, to fill out special order forms to procure it, and to keep records regarding its use, making it difficult to prescribe and dispense.

Meanwhile, a film called *Tell Your Children* was financed by a church in 1936 to teach parents about the dangers of cannabis use. Soon after the film was shot, it was purchased and renamed *Reefer Madness* for distribution on the exploitation film circuit in 1938.

On the hemp front, machines had finally been developed to quickly process the hemp hurds (the woody material in the center of the hemp stalk) and the fiber so it could be used to produce textiles, paper, and fuel. In fact, a 1938 article in *Popular Mechanics* magazine touted hemp as the new 'Billion Dollar Crop' because of this new technology for separating the fibers. But the manufacture of cotton for cloth and trees for paper was so firmly established that hemp production was being phased out and it was too late.

While there is a lot of speculation on the influence of Pierre S. DuPont and William Randolph Hearst on this effort to bring down hemp and cannabis, it looks like the only uses for cannabis at the time were for medicine, bird seed, and paint. However, Hearst owned the paper, and DuPont was developing patents on petroleum-based fibers, particularly nylon, so it was in their best interest to criminalize cannabis.

It didn't take long after the Tax Act for cannabis to be removed from the *U.S. Pharmacopoeia* because of the persistent concerns about its potential to cause harm. So, that essentially ended the cultivation of hemp in the US.

However, in 1942, the Japanese invasion of the Philippines cut off the U.S. supply of Manila hemp that was used for rope. To ensure that there would be enough rope to fight the war, the U.S. government immediately distributed 400,000 pounds of hemp seeds to farmers, who were required to attend showings of the USDA's *Hemp for*

Victory movie and campaign to grow hemp in the US to support the war effort. The farmers grew and harvested more than 150,000 acres of hemp. After the war, however, hemp was banned once again.

With the exception of that brief time during the war, hemp was assumed to be marijuana and all cannabis was criminalized throughout most of the western world. The US Congress passed *The Boggs Act* in 1951, which amended the *Narcotic Drugs Import and Export Act* to penalize the possession of marijuana.

In 1970, with the passage of the *Controlled Substances Act*, marijuana was further classified by Congress as a Schedule I drug. Marijuana met that criteria because of its THC content, which they termed a "psychoactive hallucinogenic substance with a high potential for abuse." Drugs in Schedule I are distinguished as having no currently accepted medicinal use in the United States. Other Schedule I drugs include heroin, LSD, mescaline, and methaqualone (Quaaludes).

Marijuana is still listed as a Schedule 1 drug, while commercial hemp farming was deregulated in the fall of 2018, laying the groundwork for commercialization of hemp and hemp products, so long as they do not contain more than .3% THC. Now it is up to state and local governments to revamp their laws to enable hemp to be a viable crop and product in their locales.

So, how can a state legalize recreational marijuana if it's a Federal Crime to do so?

I wondered how, if it is against Federal regulations to use cannabis in a particular state, can it be grown and sold in that state? The answer is that the Tenth Amendment allows states to opt out of participating in a law or assisting in enforcement in any way, leaving federal officials to do the heavy lifting themselves. Thus, the fact that the federal government has criminalized conduct does not mean that the state, in turn, must also criminalize or prosecute that same conduct. However, the Federal Government can come into a state to enforce its laws any time it wants to.

Fortunately, because hemp is now deregulated on the federal level, most local and state governments are catching on and the hemp industry is poised for tremendous growth, regardless of a state's position on marijuana.

References for Part One

1. Angela Bacca, What's the Difference Between Hemp and Marijuana? AlterNet.org. June 5, 2014.
2. Bryan Hill, 2015. *Cannabis: A Journey Through the Ages*. May 19, http://www.ancient-origins.net.
3. *Cannabis Sativa L*. ITIS Report. www.ITIS.gov.
4. *Crime in America: A Mid-America View*. Hearings before the Select Committee on Crime, House of Representatives, 91st Cong., Ist Sess., pursuant to H. R. 17, October 11, 1969, Lincoln, Nebraska (Washington, D.C.: U.S. Government Printing Office, 1969), p. 168.
5. David F. Musto, *The History of the Marihuana Tax Act of 1937*. Arch. Gen. Psychiat. Volume 26, February 1972.
6. David P. West, *Hemp and Marijuana: Myths and Realities*. For the North American Industrial Hemp Council. http://www.naihc.org/hemp_information/content/hemp.mj.html.
7. E. Joseph Brand and Zhongzhen Zhao, *Cannabis in Chinese Medicine: Are Some Traditional Indications Referenced in Ancient Literature Related to Cannabinoids?* https://www.ncbi.nlm.nih.gov/pubmed/28344554.
8. Edward M. Brecher, *Marijuana in the New World*. The Consumers Union Report on Licit and Illicit Drugs 1972.
9. Erich Forster, *History of Hemp in Chile*.
10. Ernest Small, T*he Species Problem in Cannabis: Science & Semantics*. 1979.
11. Hudak, John, Brookings, *The Farm Bill, hemp legalization and the status of CBD: An explainer.*

https://www.brookings.edu/blog/fixgov/2018/12/14/the
-farm-bill-hemp-and-cbd-explainer/

12. IV. Robbins and F. Ramalay (1933), cited by Walton, *Marijuana*, p. 45.

13. J. Bouquet, *Cannabis. United Nations Bulletin on Narcotics*, 3 (1951): 36.

14. Jennifer Robison. *Decades of Drug Use: Data From the '60s and '70s.* http://www.gallup.com/poll/6331/decades-drug-use-data-from-60s-70s.aspx

15. Kabirvaani, *Cannabis: Religion, Myth, and Folklore.* Blog Article, Wednesday Feb 2012. https://shivahaoma.wordpress.com/2012/02/22/cannabis-sciencemyths-and-legends-i/

16. *Million-Dollar Crop*. 1938. Popular Mechanics.

17. Robert P. Walton, *Marijuana, America's New Drug Problem* (Philadelphia: J. B. Lippincott, 1938), p. 45.

18. Raymond Evans, *Hemp for Victory* (1943) https://www.youtube.com/watch?v=--y_7_YLx7M.

19. Steven Wishnia, *Debunking the Hemp Conspiracy Theory: Pot isn't illegal because the paper industry is afraid of competing with hemp -- it's because of racism and the culture wars*. AlterNet. February 20, 2008.

PART TWO

HEMP'S HEALTH

BENEFITS

Chapter 3
How Cannabinoids Work in the Body

The recent discovery of cannabinoids and the endocannabinoid system has forced the scientific community to rethink how many of our most debilitating diseases function and how they can be treated. I believe that the majority of us are deficient in cannabinoids, which are *critical to good health in humans.*

This section is full of the research that has been done on cannabinoids, and particularly cannabidiol, which is the miraculous CBD from hemp that everyone is talking about. Now, I am the type of person who wants to know *how* and *why* something works and so want you to understand some basic biology to help you decide if CBD-rich hemp oil is right for you. So, let's start with how it works.

The Discovery

The scientific discovery of the mechanism of hemp's incredible healing powers happened in 1990, when Dr. Raphael Mechoulam, a professor of medicine at the Hebrew University of Jerusalem in Israel (who just happened to also be the researcher who discovered THC), and his team were studying the brain. They found a special kind of neurotransmitter inside the brain they called a *cannabinoid.* Cannabinoids are like endorphins—the body's pain killer. The body makes its own cannabinoids and endorphins, but cannabinoids are also found in plants like cannabis—hence the name.

The team went on to discover an entire network of cannabinoids and cannabinoid receptors throughout the human body, they called the *Endocannabinoid System* or ECS. Thousands of studies now show that the endocannabinoid system is just as important as any other system, when it comes to human health. Cannabinoids and their receptors can be found in the brain, organs, glands, immune cells, and connective tissues.

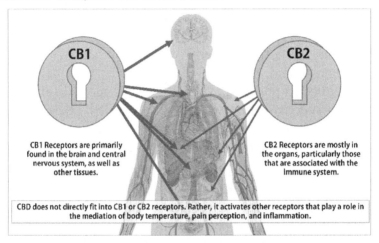

CB1 Receptors are primarily found in the brain and central nervous system, as well as other tissues.

CB2 Receptors are mostly in the organs, particularly those that are associated with the immune system.

CBD does not directly fit into CB1 or CB2 receptors. Rather, it activates other receptors that play a role in the mediation of body temperature, pain perception, and inflammation.

The ECS is critical to the function of the body and is triggered at birth when the infant suckles at the breast, receiving the cannabinoids in breast milk. These cannabinoids help bond the baby to its mother.

Unfortunately, current estimates indicate that only 13% of medical schools in the United States cover the endocannabinoid system in their curriculum, which may be why you or your doctor may not know about this.

What the ECS Does

Dr. Mechoulam found that the primary role of the ECS is the regulation of homeostasis. Homeostasis is defined as the body's ability to maintain stable internal conditions that are necessary for survival. The ECS helps to keep the body's hormones in balance. This is very important because when our hormones are out of balance, things go wrong. The truth is that this critical system impacts our entire organism, which is why its dysfunction and imbalance may lead to a variety of diseases related to the immune and nervous systems. These conditions often involve inflammation, pain, and nausea.

Each hormone in your body is responsible for a couple of functions and, together, they are responsible for your overall state of health and well-being. Your hormones contribute to your sense of identity. They are essentially a bridge between your mind and your body. You say, "I *am* tired, alert, energetic, happy, or depressed." Each of these states is dependent upon hormone balance. A quick look at the 'list of hormones' in *Wikipedia* will give you all of the hormones, what they do, and what tissue they come from. This is a mind-blowing list.

CBD impacts neurotransmitters, which are hormones that transmit signals from one neuron (brain cell) to another neuron, muscle cell, or gland cell. You have probably heard of some of them. For example, *serotonin* affects mood, appetite, and sleep, *norepinephrine* affects stress and blood pressure, *dopamine* is involved in cognition, motor control, motivation, and reward mechanisms, *glutamate* is involved in memory, *endorphins* control your response to pain, and one I had never heard of before, is *enkephalin* which, along with endorphin, regulates whether or not the body feels pain.

31

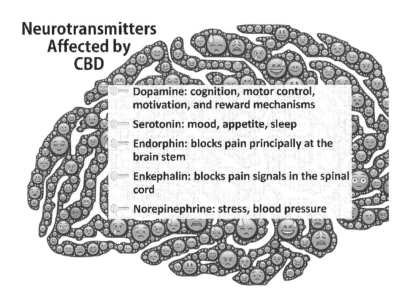

Neurotransmitters Affected by CBD

Dopamine: cognition, motor control, motivation, and reward mechanisms

Serotonin: mood, appetite, sleep

Endorphin: blocks pain principally at the brain stem

Enkephalin: blocks pain signals in the spinal cord

Norepinephrine: stress, blood pressure

Cannabinoids

There are three distinct types of cannabinoids; those that the body produces (endocannabinoids), those that come from plants (phytocannabinoids), and those that are made in the laboratory (synthetic cannabinoids).

Endocannabinoids affect the release of various neurotransmitters in the peripheral and neural tissues and support communication and coordination between various types of cells. They play a key role in inflammation, insulin sensitivity, and fat and energy metabolism.

Synthetic cannabinoids, primarily THC, have been used by researchers to obtain more detailed insight into how cannabinoids work as a potential drug.

Phytocannabinoids come from plants and interact with the endocannabinoid system. The primary source of phytocannabinoids is cannabis but other sources include:

- Coneflower (Echinacea)
- Electric Daisy (Acmella Oleracea)
- Helichrysum Umbraculigerum

- Liverwort (Radula Marginata)
- Chocolate (Theobroma Cacao)
- Black Pepper (Piper Nigrum)

After cannabinoids were discovered to have such a vital role in mammalian biology, the US government decided to get ahead of the game and patented them in 1999. Their goal was to provide a whole new class of non-psychoactive antioxidant drugs that have particular use as neuroprotective agents. Here is an excerpt from the patent:

*"Cannabinoids have been found to have **antioxidant properties**, unrelated to NMDA receptor antagonism. This new-found property makes cannabinoids useful in the treatment and prophylaxis of wide variety of oxidation associated diseases, such as ischemic, **age-related, inflammatory, and autoimmune diseases**. The cannabinoids are found to have particular application as **neuroprotectants**, for example in limiting neurological damage following ischemic insults, such as stroke and trauma, or in the **treatment of neurodegenerative diseases**, such as Alzheimer's disease, Parkinson's disease, and HIV dementia. Non-psychoactive cannabinoids, such as cannabidiol, are particularly advantageous to use because they avoid toxicity that is encountered with psychoactive cannabinoids at high doses useful in the method of the present invention."*

United States Patent 6,630,507. October 1999.

Cannabinoid Receptors

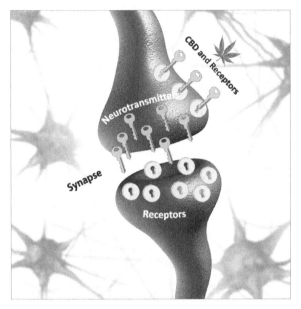

Cannabinoids, as well as terpenes, are chemicals that provide effects by inserting themselves into receptors in the tissues and cells of the endocannabinoid system, like a lock and key. In fact, cannabinoids target specific receptors on the surface of cells in different areas of the body, and so have different functions. There are two receptors in the ECS called CB1 and CB2. These receptors and the flow of cannabinoids work the same way that neurotransmitters do in the brain; like a lock and key when flooded with triggering chemicals—in this case, cannabinoids. While, so far, only CB1 and CB2 have been found, many researchers and scientists speculate that other receptors beyond CB1 and CB2 may exist.

CB1 Receptors

CB1 receptors in the central nervous system combine with the nerve cells in the brain and central nervous system to help regulate the body's biochemistry. Endocannabinoids and phytocannabinoids bind to these receptor points. THC possesses a very high binding affinity with CB1 receptors in the brain, central nervous system, connective tissues, gonads, glands, and related organs. This is one reason why the consumption of cannabis strains containing a high amount of THC give people relief from pain, nausea, or depression. While CBD *indirectly* binds to these receptors, it also provides these benefits.

CB2 Receptors

CB2 receptors are found primarily in the peripheral nervous system and in areas of the immune system, specifically on white blood cells, in the tonsils, the thymus gland, and the spleen. They are also common in the brain, but not as densely as the CB1 sites, and occur in the gastrointestinal system in high concentrations. The intestines are responsible for about 80 per cent of the immune system, and this is where CB2 sites modulate the intestinal inflammatory response. This is why those who suffer from digestive conditions can get relief from CBD hemp oil.

Cannabidiol – The Miraculous Elixir

Cannabidiol (CBD) is a class of cannabinoids that accounts for up to 40% of the hemp plant's extract. CBD does not *directly* stimulate CB1 receptors the way that THC does, and it only somewhat stimulates CB2 receptors. Instead, **it activates other receptors that play a role in pain perception and inflammation**. CBD has been shown to activate something called anadamide, which is present in some foods and in mammalian brains, where it acts as a messenger molecule and plays a role in pain, depression, appetite, memory, and fertility.

It also neuroprotective in that it minimizes the damaging effects of THC in the brain. When researchers first studied the effects of marijuana, they used isolated THC to see the effects it had and discovered that it caused damage to certain areas of the brain. However, research done on marijuana as a whole plant, with all of its compounds in combination, showed that it did not damage the brain. They called this the *entourage effect*. This led to the discovery of CBD and led to the patent in 1999.

Cannabigerol: The Mother of CBD

Cannabigerol, or CBG, is a non-psychoactive cannabinoid which is abundant in hemp but present in low levels (usually less than 1%) in most cannabis strains. Think of it as the mother of THC and CBD. They both start out as CBG and convert during the flowering cycle.

In the body, CBG interacts with both the CB1 and CB2 receptors. It is thought to boost anandamide, the endocannabinoid that naturally increases dopamine levels and is responsible for regulating various health functions such as mood, sleep, and appetite. GABA uptake in the brain may be obstructed by CBG, making this cannabinoid a possible anti-anxiety agent and muscle relaxant. CBG may also block serotonin receptors, showing potential antidepressant traits.

I recently tried a CBG product and my experience was significant, providing me with a level of happiness and serenity that I had never experienced consistently before. This is like CBD on steroids for me.

CBG has been shown to provide a number of potential health benefits:

- neuroprotectant
- antioxidant
- antibacterial and antifungal agent,
- anti-inflammatory
- treatment of gastrointestinal disorders

36

The Entourage Effect

In 2011, Dr Ethan Russo, a preeminent cannabis researcher coined the term, *The Entourage Effect* to explain the synergy of the various compounds in the cannabis plant and how, in combination, they seem to create a greater response in the body than the individual components do alone. This is a phenomenon can be seen in other nutrient compounds as well. For example, Dr. Linus Pauling did tremendous research on Vitamin C, or ascorbic acid, and won a Nobel prize for his research. But with the discovery of bioflavonoids, or citrus complex, the true value of vitamin C was understood. Bioflavonoids are the cofactors that work synergistically with ascorbic acid to create greater benefits than does just ascorbic acid, alone.

The same is true for CBD. While the majority of the research done over the last 20 years has been on either THC or CBD isolate, we are just now discovering the benefits of the complex of compounds in the cannabis plant. So, rather than just taking CBD isolate for health, we are now discovering that full spectrum hemp oil provides greater benefits than CBD, alone.

Terpenes

While cannabidiol is the most abundant of the cannabinoids, there is also a class of phytochemicals called *terpenes* that are just as important, when we are looking at hemp as a dietary supplement. Terpenes are the fragrant oils that give plants their various aromas. The scent in all herbs and other aromatic plants is from the terpenes that waft up your nostrils. In cannabis, the terpenes are primarily secreted in the flower's sticky resin glands. Terpenes exist in hemp as well as in marijuana. According to the British Journal of Pharmacology, cannabis has about 200 different terpenes in varying concentrations in any given strain. Of these, there are about 10 primary terpenes and about 20 secondary terpenes.

Terpenes bind to receptors in your brain to give you various effects, just like cannabinoids do. Studies on terpenes from cannabis show that they are as responsible for the benefits to the body as is cannabidiol.

Terpenes maximize the impact of cannabinoids in the bloodstream. Unfortunately, the extraction process destroys many of them, so, many manufacturers are now adding specific terpenes back into the product to create a more efficacious effect. Here is a list of the most beneficial terpenes that contribute to the entourage effect of hemp oil:

Geraniol

Geraniol is the primary component in rose oil, and citronella oil (Java type). It also occurs in small quantities in geranium, lemon, hemp, and many other essential oils. Aside from its use as a flavor and aroma ingredient, scientific literature suggests geraniol has many therapeutic uses.

First, studies suggest geraniol protects against the Candida albicans fungus which causes yeast infections. It has also been shown to kill the bacteria that cause food poisoning like E. coli, Listeria, and Salmonella.

Second, it has been shown to be an antioxidant. Oxidation in cells creates free radicals that can damage human DNA and other parts of the cell, which, in turn, can contribute to aging, arteriosclerosis, and even asthma. Geraniol has been shown to be a strong free radical scavenger and neutralizer.

Finally, scientists have demonstrated that geraniol inhibits both the inflammatory response and oxidative stress in rat subjects that suffered traumatic spinal injuries.

Humulene

Humulene is found in a wide variety of plants and has been used for centuries in holistic Eastern medicinal practices. It shares the same chemical formula as β-caryophyllene but the two differ in structure. You may see literature stating that they are the same, but they are not. Many of the same plants containing β-caryophyllene—such as basil, sage, and clove—also contain humulene, and the two have very similar aromas.

Humulene and other terpenes help plants defend against pests and prevents fungal infestations while the plant is developing.

Among its benefits in animals, humulene acts as an appetite suppressant and exhibits potent anti-inflammatory and anti-tumor activity. One study showed that it may help kill cancer cells when combined with phytocannabinoids and other terpenes. In another study, it was shown to exhibit antibacterial properties, proving it, among other terpenes, to be active against the *Staphylococcus aureus* when given in small quantities.

Limonene

Limonene is primarily found in the peels of citrus fruits. It is also found in cannabis. It has been used to promote weight loss, prevent cancer, treat cancer, and treat bronchitis. It may block cancer-forming chemicals and has been shown to kill cancer cells in the laboratory.

Limonene has also been shown to be an effective anti-fungal treatment for Candida Albicans a potent antibacterial agent against E. coli and staph, and to reduce stress when inhaled as an essential oil. It also improves absorption of other terpenes and chemicals by way of the skin, mucous membranes, and digestive tract. In other words, adding limonene to a hemp cream helps it penetrate more easily.

Linalool

Linalool is a terpene found in many flowers and spices including lavender, hemp, and coriander. It is one of the substances most widely used as an essential oil to reduce stress. Linalool has been the subject of many studies, including a recent one in which scientists allowed lab rats to inhale linalool while exposing them to stressful conditions. It was reported that linalool returned elevated stress levels in the rats to near-normal conditions. It is not recommended that people eat linalool by itself, but as part of the complex of hemp oil. However, its true benefit is in its ability to reduce stress when inhaled.

Myrcene

Myrcene is also found in many essential oils and is sourced from a multitude of plants, including hops, lemongrass, chamomile, and mangos, as well as in various strains of cannabis sativa. It is one of the most abundant terpenes in cannabis.

Myrcene has been shown to support the immune system. It is a T helper type-2 immune enhancer. It has also been shown to be a potent pain reliever. In a study on subjects with migraine who used a high THC and myrcene cannabis compound, the researchers concluded, "*it reflects the potent analgesic, anti-inflammatory, and anti-emetic properties of THC, with anti-inflammatory and analgesic properties of β-caryophyllene [humulene] and βmyrcene.*" When added into a CBD rich hemp oil, myrcene can be expected to provide the same benefits.

Pinene

Pinene accounts for cannabis' familiar odor, often associated with pine trees and turpentine. αPinene is the most common naturally occurring terpenoid in cannabis and acts as both an anti-inflammatory and a bronchodilator.

A study done on subjects with bronchitis were given a compound composed of 1200 mg. pinene, limonene, and 1,8-cineole. It was concluded that the formula is *"an alternative to antibiotics for acute bronchitis without specified infective agent, without the risk to promote the development of bacterial resistance."*

Terpinolene

Terpinolene, while found in many cannabis strains, is usually present only in small amounts. When added back into a hemp oil mixture, it can have powerful effects.

Studies have shown that terpinolene has the potential to reduce the risk of heart disease when used in concert with alpha-tocopherol and beta-carotene, showing that it effectively prevents oxidation of LDL cholesterol. Another study showed that it has a role in inhibiting the growth of cancer cells.

In addition, terpinolene has been shown to be an antioxidant that can help with oxidative damage.

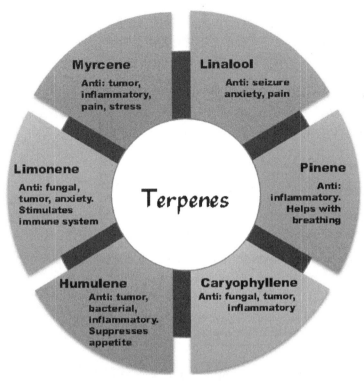

Research into terpenes is just beginning and is very exciting, when it comes to the use of plants for health maintenance.

CEDS – Clinical Endocannabinoid Deficiency Syndrome

Before your brain spins out of control trying to grasp all this science, take a minute to imagine the implications for phytocannabinoids as a dietary supplement that is just as important as vitamins or minerals. Did you know that a lack of certain vitamins or minerals can lead to diseases like scurvy, beriberi, or even blindness?

What if many health conditions are due to a deficiency of cannabinoids?

Cannabinoid deficiency is becoming more accepted as the probable cause of several illnesses, including anxiety, clinical insomnia, anger management issues, depression, conditions associated with inflammation throughout your body like arthritis, fibromyalgia, bone loss, migraine, and irritable bowel syndrome. The official name for this is *Clinical Endocannabinoid Deficiency Syndrome* or CEDS.

A growing number of scientists believe that low levels of endocannabinoids (the kind your body makes) are the root cause of these conditions. There is scientific evidence suggesting that a lack of endocannabinoids plays a role in *inflammation, insulin sensitivity, and fat and energy metabolism.*

Further, scientists have discovered that when people undergo trauma, the body creates more endocannabinoid receptors to manage the need for specific neurotransmitters. A study published in 2013 in *Molecular Psychiatry* showed via brain imaging, that people with PTSD have markedly lower concentrations of the endocannabinoid anandamide than do people without PTSD.

If the body cannot make enough cannabinoids to fill these increased receptors, then it stands to reason that there is a deficiency that requires exogenous cannabinoids (from external sources).

The theory of clinical endocannabinoid deficiency is also based on the concept that, because many brain disorders such as Alzheimer's and Parkinson's disease, as well as depression and PTSD, are associated with neurotransmitter deficiencies, they could be correlated with a comparable deficiency in endocannabinoids. Here's why:

1. There is a lack of cannabinoids in the food supply.
2. There is a tendency for endocannabinoids to be deficient or degrade within the human body.

3. Supplementing with cannabinoids can reduce inflammation and protect critical cells against oxidation in the brain and other areas of the body.

4. Therefore, there is a deficiency of cannabinoids in the body that phytocannabinoids can resolve.

So, doesn't it make sense that a diet rich in phytocannabinoids like CBG, CBD-rich hemp oil, and hemp seeds might offset these deficiencies?

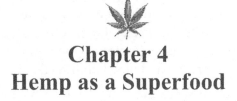

Chapter 4
Hemp as a Superfood

Now that you know that your body is deficient in cannabinoids you will probably conclude, like I did, that this is not only something you can use to treat a condition, but that this is something you should be taking every day for *health maintenance.*

I believe that because the cannabis plant contains 483 compounds that are unique to cannabis and 140 that are in common with other plants, we have just touched the surface when it comes to the miracles this plant can perform and more amazing properties will be discovered.

Hemp and hemp-derived edible products can be considered as both foods and as dietary supplements, depending on how they are processed and consumed. They can also be classified as medicines, depending on the medical claims made.

Hemp is so nutritious that people could survive on just it and water! If you have been to the health store in recent years you know that hemp has attained the ranks of a staple food. Like quinoa and soy, hemp seeds contain all the essential amino and fatty acids that are necessary for human life. Food products made from hemp now include milk, flour, cereal, frozen waffles, nut butters, cooking oil, and all sorts of baked goods, in addition to protein powder and hemp seeds. Hemp has a nutty flavor and pairs well with all kinds of other ingredients and flavors.

Imagine that by simply adding hemp to your diet, you could lower your cholesterol, reduce your risk of dementia and cancer, and even put you in a better mood, all without the side effects of drugs. That is the power of *Superfoods*. You are probably eating some of them without knowing it. Superfoods are unprocessed nutrient-rich foods which are especially beneficial for health and well-being. Examples are kale, spinach, omega 3-rich fish, certain nuts and seeds, and berries—and now hemp seeds!

Whole hemp seeds are considered to be a superfood. They are a nutritional powerhouse that tastes good and provides a rich source of 44 percent fatty acids in perfect balance, 33 percent of protein as a complete amino acid profile, 12 percent of both soluble and insoluble fiber, and carbohydrates. In fact, they provide everything humans need in their diet. Let's look at the specific nutritional components of hemp so you can get a grasp of the benefits beyond those of CBD hemp oil.

As just a food source, alone, think about what that can do in places in the world where people are starving and malnourished?

The Nutrients in Hemp Seeds

Protein

Hemp seeds are high in protein, containing all nine essential amino acids. Despite what you may read, some of them are not present in enough of a quantity to meet the criteria for essential human nutrition. The only plant source with a more complete protein profile is soy.

What is exceptional about hemp seed protein is that it is so easy to digest. About 60% of it is composed of *edistin*. Edestin is a type of plant protein similar to the protein found in human blood so hemp protein is very easily digested. Another one-third of hemp's protein is albumin, which is another high-quality protein also found in egg whites. **There are no other plants that have this combination of proteins.** Hemp protein powder has higher levels of protein than the seeds, alone do. The powder is what is left over after the shells and the oil are removed from the seeds. It provides 50 to 75% more protein then either flax or chia.

Fats

Humans need twenty different fatty acids in their diets to maintain optimum health. Our bodies can manufacture all but two of these twenty. These two are called essential fatty acids (EFAs) because we need to get them from food. They are called omega-3 and omega-6. The ideal ratio is four omega-3's to one omega-6 to offset the imbalances that research has shown to be a problem with our western diet.

Hemp seeds are one of the most balanced sources of omega-3 and omega-6. Hemp oil is the richest known source of polyunsaturated essential fatty acids (the "good" fats), including *gamma linoleic acid* (GLA), which is also found in mother's milk, borage, black currant seed, and evening primrose oils. While the body can manufacture GLA from other fats, the process requires an enzyme that some people lack so getting it directly from hemp is ideal.

Carbohydrates

Carbohydrates are traditionally considered a source for energy because they convert to glucose when eaten. Scientists call them 'sugars' and any words that start with 'glyco' or 'gluco' refer to their carbohydrate structure. Glucose is the food the brain lives on, and without enough from carbohydrates in the diet, the body will rob muscle and convert it to glucose to keep the brain alive. Of course, I don't know anyone who isn't getting enough carbohydrate in their diet; do you?

There is more to the story, however. Some carbohydrates are sweet, and some are not. If it's not a fat or a protein, it's a carbohydrate! So, fiber is a carbohydrate, as well as saps, gums, and starches. Biochemists in the 1980's discovered that there are 'sugar' molecules that don't readily convert to energy or glucose that are called *glyconutrients*. Glyconutrients are metabolized into molecular building blocks for cellular communication called *glycans*. All living cells are coated with glycans. They are one of the four fundamental classes of macromolecules that make up all living systems.

Because these glycans are so necessary, it is important to eat foods with glyconutrients, so the body has the raw materials to build them. Hemp is a great source of glyconutrients. It contains thirteen glyconutrients, including *galactose, arabinose,* and *mannose* which build cellular communication and immune system structures, plus two others you may have heard of: galactosamine and glucosamine.

These carbohydrate molecules are responsible for how well our immune and endocrine systems function and how well they regulate inflammation. By eating hemp seeds and CBD hemp oil, you are getting the important glyconutrients you need for your cells to communicate more efficiently!

Fiber

Everybody knows that we should all eat more fiber. Fiber aids digestion, improves the absorption of nutrients and helps the body maintain insulin effectiveness while decreasing the risk of certain diseases. Not only are we supposed to eat more fiber, but we should be eating more soluble fiber, as that is really the gut-healthy fiber we should be after. The body builds the immune system using the fiber in the gut, so increasing fiber can dramatically support overall health. The modern western diet lacks the recommended 25–30g/day of fiber that we need.

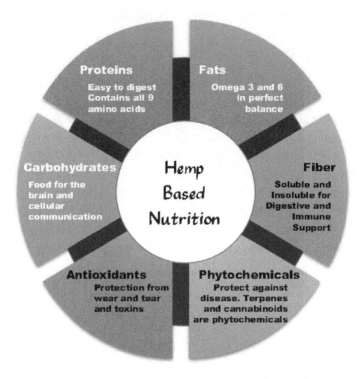

The fiber is in the seed shells. Adding *whole* hemp seeds, hemp flour, or hemp protein powder (be sure to check the label for the fiber content) as part of your regular diet will ensure that you are getting the fiber you need. Whole hemp seed averages 16 grams of fiber in a serving, which means that you just need to eat a couple of handfuls of seeds by adding them to your smoothies and salads, and you are good to go. Just remember, shelled hemp seeds do not have any fiber, to speak of.

Phytochemicals

Phytochemicals (chemicals from plants) are natural bioactive compounds that have specific effects on the function of cells. *They are not vitamins, minerals, proteins, fats, or carbohydrates.* Phytochemicals work with nutrients and dietary fiber to protect against disease. Cannabinoids and terpenes in hemp are phytochemicals.

Antioxidants

Antioxidants are a class of phytochemicals that protects the body from wear and tear, while strengthening the immune system, muscles, bones, and skin. They do this by de-activating cell-damaging free radicals that form as we use energy, age, and are exposed to sun, pollutants, and other toxic chemicals. This production of free radicals is called *oxidative stress*, which is believed to be the root cause of many health conditions, including neurodegenerative, cardiovascular, and inflammatory diseases, as well as certain forms of cancer.

While it is breaking down the body, oxidative stress speeds up the aging process by altering the structure and function of all the body's cells. Oxidative stress is to the body what rust is to iron. So, the more antioxidants that are present in the body, the less damage free radicals can cause. CBD-rich hemp oil has been shown to have antioxidant effects and act as a neuroprotective agent that minimizes the effects of oxidative stress.

Chapter 5
Hemp Oil as a Dietary Supplement

Hemp is not only a nutritious food, it is also a dietary supplement, in its own right. Researchers are continuously amazed by the number and variety of health benefits they are discovering in CBD hemp oil. It makes sense for anyone to understand these health benefits and incorporate it into a healthy lifestyle plan.

Before I start this section, I want you to be very clear that *supplements are not medicine,* in the legal sense. Most people use them like medicine, however. You can go to any health food store and listen as a customer talks to a clerk, asking about which supplement will help with their health-compromised condition. This is because we have become so oriented to the allopathic or medical model that we don't see health in terms of a whole but rather as a cause-effect, symptom-treatment issue.

I am about to show you several studies that were done on either rats or humans to demonstrate the benefits of CBD. Doing this kind of research can be challenging for people who are holistic or interested in CBD-rich hemp oil alone because the majority of the studies were initially done using THC-based cannabis and later with pure cannabidiol. We need to distinguish between the benefits of THC cannabis and CBD hemp oil. Because there is so much conversation these days about medical marijuana, people are confusing CBD with marijuana and you need to understand the benefits of CBD without THC. If you live in an area where medical marijuana is available, you can research the array of products that combine both, but for most us, CBD-rich hemp oil is enough.

Let's review what we know so far:

1. The endocannabinoid system is involved in virtually every function of the body–both in the peripheral and central nervous systems as well as the organs.
2. The types of cannabinoids that exist on the immune system's receptors and cells can play a major role in maintaining immunity.
3. CBD impacts the neuroendocrine system and the immune system because these systems interact with the endocannabinoid system.

So, because the ECS helps maintain equilibrium in the body, it is important to nourish yourself with CBD-rich hemp oil so you can maintain your health and keep life-threatening conditions from rearing their ugly heads. Even though the body seeks out its own endocannabinoids first, anyone who wants to maintain health and well-being should supplement with plant-based nutrients if they want to correct the imbalances of life's stresses, manage toxins, and offset dietary deficiencies. If we give our bodies the foods they need to support our systems, we can reduce and often eliminate chronic illness and medical bills.

There are a lot of compounds in hemp that impact health in ways you haven't thought about before. While some ingredients in supplements will help you with an array of disorders, the case I am making here is that **even if you feel great and don't need to 'treat' anything, you still need to replace the nutrients that are missing in your diet to optimize your health and help fight the toxins you are exposed to each day.** I believe that cannabidiol is a nutrient in the same way that vitamin D is for health maintenance and the prevention of disease.

Now that so much research has been done on CBD-rich hemp oil as a dietary supplement, anyone should feel confident that it will promote health and help prevent disease. This is very encouraging for those of us who are not amendable to the whims of the pharmacological community and prefer to use plants to support health.

The US patent on cannabinoids is very clear as to the health benefits of cannabis. It states that non-psychoactive cannabinoids such as cannabidiol are particularly advantageous to use because *"they avoid toxicity that is encountered with psychoactive cannabinoids at high doses."* What this means is that while there are distinct medical benefits from using cannabinoids including THC, there are also benefits in the use of cannabidiol hemp oil as a dietary supplement.

Researchers focus their attention on disease because they can provide clear evidence of improvement more easily than they can prove that a substance in the form of a dietary supplement prevents ill health. When a medical researcher can show that a natural or synthetic compound improves a 'medical condition' that is observable, he or she can receive funding from drug companies. That is why most of the research done on CBD has focused on the treatment or amelioration of disease and its why the US has a patent on it.

So, even though the research was done to show the benefits in terms of a potential drug, when a natural compound shows statistical significance in the laboratory, it makes sense that it will also work as a dietary supplement.

My point is, that we can look at the research on CBD and medical conditions and assume that it will work as a dietary supplement *before* it becomes a medical condition.

Prevention Instead of Treatment: That's the Name of the Game

CBD-Rich Hemp Oil to Manage Stress and Support Cognition

For me personally, one of the biggest benefits of CBD-rich hemp oil is its ability to reduce stress in the body and mind. Think about how your body feels when you are under stress. Some people feel a generalized tightness in their body. Some start yelling at people, especially the ones they love. Some feel the need to run away and hide. Some start to feel defeated and quit. Pay attention to what's happening inside your body both physically and mentally when you are under stress and then take CBD-rich hemp oil to experience the difference in your ability to manage it.

We have a culture that is very stress promoting. We have financial pressures, job pressures, family issues, and then, to compound it all, we have health issues with which we are dealing. Stress is the number one reason why our bodies start to fall apart. Many hormones and biochemical processes are generated as the result of stress, particularly inflammation. Inflammation can be said to be the underlying cause of every human disease. If we learn how to manage our stress better, inflammation will be reduced, and our health will vastly improve.

Robert Sapolsky, PhD, has spent three decades investigating the role of stress on human health. The PBS documentary *"Stress: Portrait of a Killer"* illustrates how prolonged exposure to stress can ruin your health in a multitude of ways. Common health conditions that are caused or worsened by stress include heart disease, hypertension, impaired immune function, infertility, joint pain, and mental illness.

A little stress is good and can be motivational. The point at which stress becomes bad is when you feel you can't control your environment and become overwhelmed because you feel powerless to accomplish your dreams and goals. When you are in such a state, your adrenal system shuts down, your immune system is compromised, and your health begins to deteriorate.

Because I was trained as a psychologist, I understand that emotional and cognitive states determine health outcomes in terms of well-being. Conversely, health can positively mediate or prevent depression and anxiety. So, *if there is a dietary supplement that supports emotional and cognitive health, then a person who is dealing with stressors that impact their ability to be happy, healthy, and productive should use it!* I am not saying that a supplement alone will resolve the causes of the stress, in most cases. I am saying that it will *reduce* the stress so that the individual can do the inner work to resolve the causes.

Let's look at some areas of health that CBD impacts:

Anxiety

One of the ways to assess stress or fear in the body is to measure cortisol levels in the blood. Cortisol is one of the key hormones involved in inflammation and stress. Cortisol levels are heightened when animals are under extreme stress. A group of Brazilian researchers investigated the effect of CBD doses on cortisol levels in humans and found that CBD decreased cortisol levels significantly more than a placebo. CBD subjects also reported a sedative effect from the treatment.

Social anxiety is a medical term for people who are nervous in social situations. CBD has been shown to reduce anxiety in people with social anxiety disorder and it may also be effective for panic disorder, obsessive compulsive disorder, and post-traumatic stress disorder. The greater social anxiety a person has, the more difficult it is for them to maintain eye contact or initiate and maintain a conversation. While everyone experiences situational shyness at some point, social anxiety disorder is a medical condition that can be attributed to about half of the people who have any social fears.

One group of researchers studied the effects of a simulated public speaking test on healthy control people who took either CBD or a placebo ninety minutes before making a speech. These people had never been treated for social anxiety. The results showed that those people who took the CBD **improved their speech performance and significantly decreased their stress** when anticipating their speech. The placebo group showed greater anxiety, cognitive impairment, and discomfort. *They did MRI scans of the subjects afterward that revealed that CBD triggers activity in the areas of the brain that are linked to anxiety and emotion.*

Sleep

Have you noticed that when you have more stress, your quality of sleep is impaired? Sleeping well is fundamental to health and well-being. People typically underestimate the health value of sleep. We know we need it to feel rested, but sleep has an additional function that is critical to your health. During deep sleep, your body repairs itself. Your brain produces hormones and enzymes that you need to regulate every bodily system while you're sleeping. This is the time when the brain and the immune system does its work, so if you're awake and not sleeping well, you're missing out on the opportunity for your body to help regulate your health.

Studies of blood tests have shown that CBD impacts the dopamine levels in the bloodstream during sleep. This leads to a better, more relaxed sleep. Several studies have shown that CBD-rich hemp oil can benefit insomnia.

CBD-rich hemp oil doesn't just make falling asleep easier, it also influences the sleep cycle. Sleep is divided into multiple cycles with distinct phases. CBD-rich hemp oil increases the third phase, which is that of deep sleep. In addition, it decreases the duration of REM sleep, which is a phase of light sleep during which dreaming occurs. REM sleep is necessary but too much of it causes fitful, light sleep. By reducing REM sleep, people dream less, memory is improved, and symptoms of depression are reduced.

In a 1981 Brazilian study, researchers assigned 15 insomniacs to a CBD dose (ranging between 40 mg and 160 mg), a placebo, or a drug used to relieve anxiety and insomnia. With the highest CBD dose, sleep significantly increased, although dream recall was reduced, when compared to the placebo, indicating a deeper sleep.

Breaks with Reality

Psychosis is a loss of contact with reality. Step psychosis back and you have neurosis, which is depression, anxiety, obsessive behavior, or hypochondria, but without the radical loss of touch with reality. Research in this area shows that CBD has a **pharmacological profile like that of certain antipsychotic drugs**. People with psychotic episodes regularly show signs of endocannabinoid deficiency. They have fewer CB2 cannabinoid receptors than do healthy people. They also have lower levels of the enzymes that enable the endocannabinoid system to function properly.

CBD-Rich Hemp Oil for Pain and Inflammation

According to the *New England Journal of Medicine*, more than 30% of Americans have some form of either acute or chronic pain and over 40% of older adults in the US have chronic pain. There are three classes of drugs that work to reduce pain: over the counter analgesics like aspirin and NSAIDS, corticosteroids, and opiates.

The numbers are staggering. Sales in the US alone for OTC analgesics in 2016 was over four billion dollars! An estimated 9 million epidural steroid injections are performed annually in the US to relieve back and joint pain. Opiate use has become pandemic, often triggered by pain medication that is prescribed after an accident or surgery. Opioid analgesics are now the most commonly prescribed class of medications in the United States. In 2014 alone, U.S. retail pharmacies dispensed 245 million prescriptions for opioid pain relievers.

In our attempts to manage pain with drugs, our population is experiencing adverse side effects leading to death and increased levels of addiction. This, if nothing else, is one of the most important reasons why people need to become educated about hemp and CBD.

When it comes to anti-inflammatory effects, CBD is a clear winner over drugs. A *proinflammatory cytokine* is a type of signaling molecule that is excreted from immune cells and certain other cell types that promote inflammation. A 2006 study showed a significant reduction of blood levels of *pro*-inflammatory cytokines when using CBD. So, **CBD reduces the levels of inflammation in the body**. Externally, it can be used as a topical ointment that relieves nerve pain and tingling in hands and feet.

Studies even suggest that CBD-rich hemp oil can reduce arthritis pain. A 2012 study published in the *Journal of Experimental Medicine* found that CBD significantly suppressed chronic inflammatory and neuropathic pain in rodents without causing analgesic tolerance. In other words, **you don't need to continue to increase the dose to get a response.**

CBD has been shown to connect to the same brain synapses as opioids. This is big news because **when used in conjunction with an opiate, CBD will reduce the likelihood of opiate dependence.**

The Medical Benefits of CBD-Rich Hemp Oil

Now, while the following are medical conditions, I felt that it was important to add them to this discussion on prevention using dietary supplements. If you are not sick and do not have a medical condition, then using CBD-rich hemp oil as a dietary supplement is perfect for you. However, there has been so much preliminary research done on the medical benefits of cannabis, it cannot be swept under the rug, even in a hemp book! So, check out this fascinating section on how CBD-rich hemp oil may help with certain diseases.

CBD and the Heart

Heart disease is the leading cause of death in the US, with cancer as a close second. So, if CBD can protect the cardiovascular system the way it helps with pain, we have another miracle from hemp. A review of the literature in the *British Journal of Clinical Pharmacology* suggests several benefits to the cardiovascular system when taking CBD hemp oil. First, "CBD has direct actions on isolated arteries, causing both acute and time-dependent vasorelaxation." *Vasorelaxation* is the expansion of blood vessels so that more blood can flow at a lower pressure. Restricted blood vessels contribute to problems in heart disease. Researchers found that **CBD relaxes blood vessels, so blood can flow more easily.**

CBD also **protects against heart tissue damage** caused when the blood supply returns to the tissue after a period of *ischemia*—which is a lack of oxygen—and against *cardiomyopathy*, like an enlarged heart or other heart tissue damage associated with diabetes.

Finally, CBD **protects against the blood vessel damage** caused by a high glucose environment,

59

inflammation, or the induction of type 2 diabetes in animal models. One of the most common examples of this benefit is in diabetes, where vision and circulation problems cause pain and damage.

If you are genetically predisposed to heart-related conditions then I highly recommend using CBD on a daily basis.

CBD and Diabetes

According to the *Centers for Disease Control*, almost ten percent of the people in the US are diabetic and another third of Americans are *pre-diabetic*. This is a phenomenal number of people whose health is adversely impacted by their diet and lifestyle and, as the population grows, this will only become a larger issue. But there is hope. For example, a 2006 study found that CBD treatment significantly reduced the incidence of diabetes in non-obese diabetic mice from an incidence of 86 percent in non-treated mice to an incidence of 30 percent in CBD-treated mice. That's a 56 percent reduction!

That news is very helpful for people with diabetes but what about people who are pre-diabetic? In 2013, the *American Journal of Medicine* published a study that highlighted the impact of marijuana use on glucose, insulin, and insulin resistance among U.S. adults. The study included 4,657 adult men and women from the *National Health and Nutritional Examination Survey* from 2005 to 2010. 579 of the subjects were current marijuana users and 1,975 were past users. The researchers found that current marijuana use was associated with 16 percent lower fasting insulin levels. They also found significant associations between marijuana use and smaller waist circumferences.

Now, this does not necessarily mean that CBD alone will have the same effect, but when you factor in the anti-inflammatory effects of CBD it is a sure bet it will help.

Chronic inflammation plays a key role in the development of insulin resistance, which leads to type 2 diabetes. Consequently, because CBD reduces inflammation it could also help improve the body's metabolism.

CBD and Cancer

We all have cancer cells in our bodies at any time. These cells proliferate depending upon the health of our immune systems. The way the body eliminates them is through a process called *apoptosis*, which is damaged cell suicide. If the process of apoptosis fails, the mutated cells can duplicate rapidly and invade the adjacent cells, which is what we call cancer. When our immune systems are healthy, they can recognize damaged cells and trigger apoptosis. One of the most exciting areas of research on CBD is its effect on cancer.

There are lots of studies on CBD and how it protects the body against cancer. In one study, investigators found that CBD protected DNA from oxidative damage and increased endocannabinoid levels. *The National Cancer Institute* details several studies into the anti-tumor effects of CBD. One study in mice and rats suggests CBD *"may have a protective effect against the development of certain types of tumors."* It may do this by inducing apoptosis, inhibiting cancer cell growth, and by controlling and inhibiting the spread of cancer cells.

Another study done by *California Pacific Medical Center* suggests that CBD "turns off" the gene involved in the spread of breast cancer. They also found that CBD targets breast tumor cells and leaves healthy cells alone. Breast cancer experiments show that the number of cancer cells diminishes as more CBD is used.

CBD has been shown to be non-toxic in doses as high as 700 milligrams per day for 6 weeks, which means that it can be used for prolonged treatment and has potential for being developed into a drug for the treatment of cancer.

Not only does the research show that CBD is effective in fighting breast cancer cells, it also suggests that **it can be used to inhibit the invasion of cancer cells in the lung and colon.** Plus, it has demonstrated **anti-tumor properties in brain tumor studies as well as prostate, liver, pancreatic tumors, and even leukemia,** where it has been proven that cannabinoids inhibit the growth of cancer cells.

Another critical issue when it comes to the treatment of cancer, is its effect on the reaction to chemotherapy. **CBD eases nausea and vomiting.** Researchers have found that in low doses, it suppresses toxin-induced vomiting, but in high doses it increases nausea or has no effect. So, low doses of CBD are enough to ease the nausea from chemotherapy.

CBD, Seizures, and Other Neurological Disorders

Epilepsy is a condition that has shown a particularly beneficial response to CBD hemp oil. A 2014 survey conducted at *Stanford University* was given to parents belonging to a *Facebook* group dedicated to sharing information about the use of cannabidiol-enriched cannabis to treat their child's seizures. There was an average of 12 anti-epileptic drugs tried before using CBD. 84 percent of the parents reported a reduction in their child's seizure frequency while taking CBD hemp oil. Of these, two reported complete seizure freedom, eight reported a greater than 80 percent reduction in seizure frequency, and six reported a 25–60 percent seizure reduction.

Later in 2014, researchers reported on preliminary results of a study involving children with treatment-resistant epilepsies. People received a purified 98 percent CBD-rich hemp oil extract. After 3 months of treatment, 39 percent of the subjects had a greater than a 50 percent reduction in their seizures.

These preliminary results support the animal studies and survey reports that CBD may be a promising solution for treatment-resistant epilepsy and it is well-tolerated in doses up to 25 milligrams per kilogram of body weight. That is—if you weigh 100 pounds, you can take 1,136 mg of CBD per day and do just fine.

The facts; this is by no means a panacea. Between 10-15 percent of severe childhood epileptics who are given CBD oil products experience a near complete cessation of seizures; most improve (with a decrease but not total elimination of seizures); and some children have worse seizures when they take CBD.

Another thing to remember is that the dosages reported being used are much greater than what you would normally get in a typical 300-1500mg bottle, so find a source that helps with higher dosage access.

Chapter 6
What to Look for in a Hemp Oil Product

Before you make a financial commitment to a CBD-rich hemp oil product, educate yourself on what to look for, in terms of quality and price, so you can make sure you are getting the best product for the money. Here are some things to look for when deciding if the product you are buying is going to deliver what it says it will: safety, standardization, extraction, and the delivery system.

Is it Safe?

Many products on the market can contain pesticides, herbicides, and mold. So be sure to check the product for the following:

1. **Testing** using equipment that measures toxin levels. Hemp takes up toxins in the soil and water, so the growing conditions need to be controlled to prevent these toxins from showing up in the product. Even though hemp requires little to no pesticides, the soil on which it is grown may have residual toxins and heavy metals from the past or from the water being used for irrigation.

2. **Organic soil** – It goes without saying that the quality of the soil determines the quality of the hemp and other food products.

3. **GMP Standards** - GMP stands for Good Manufacturing Practices. In the US, the FDA specifies

that GMP for dietary supplements means that the dietary supplement consistently meets the established specifications for identity, purity, strength, composition, and limits on contaminants, and has been manufactured, packaged, labeled, and held under conditions to prevent adulteration. Check for GMP certification.

Is it Standardized?

If you grind up a plant—or in this case plant oil—and you put it in a pill or potion, what do you get? That depends on where it was grown, when it was grown, what the soil and water was like, and how it was processed. To make a high-quality product with a good shelf life, you need to ensure that each dose is consistent from batch to batch. That is called standardization. There are a couple of ways that consumers can be assured that the product they are taking is standardized. The first way is to know that the company providing the product has a state-of-the-art laboratory where the product is tested. Transparency, in terms of the manufacturing process is critical to providing the consumer with standardization assurance. The second way is for the company to provide quality assurance data from a 3rd party lab and other certified sources.

How is the Product Made?

In an effort to provide efficacious CBD products, companies have tried different methods for ending up with a standardized amount of product per dose. First, research has shown that ingesting pure CBD crystals does not render the same benefits as full spectrum CBD hemp oil, which has been minimally processed. Some processing methods destroy the terpenes, other cannabinoids, and the phytochemicals that work synergistically with CBD. So, the first thing to look for is a full spectrum product that contains the terpenes as well as a demonstrable amount of CBD per dose.

How is the CBD Extracted?

To get the most bioavailable and standardized amount of CBD in a product, the extraction process must be considered. There are many ways to extract CBD from the hemp plant. Some methods are safer and more effective than others. Some are less expensive than others. Let's look at the several ways that processors extract CBD from the plant.

CO2 Extraction

CO2 extraction is possibly the optimal extraction method. The CO2 method uses carbon dioxide under high pressure and extremely low temperatures to isolate, preserve, and maintain the purity of the oil and the terpenes. However, the equipment is expensive, so you might have to pay a bit more for CBD-rich hemp oil processed this way. Depending on the way it is processed, it may or may not retain the chlorophyll, which some people regard as having a bad taste. Given that CO2 is a naturally-occurring pure chemical substance, it leaves behind no residue.

Ethanol (Solvent-based) Extraction

This process uses chemical solvents like butane, hexane, alcohol, or other ethanol to extract the CBD from the hemp plant. This is a less expensive process than CO2 extraction and the resulting product may leave behind a residue which can be harmful to people whose immune systems are already compromised unless measures are taken to remove any residue. High grade grain alcohol can be used to create high quality cannabis oil. But this extraction method destroys the plant waxes, which may or may not have health benefits. It is also flammable.

Delivery Systems

There are numerous companies on the market these days that promote their CBD products using confusing marketing language. So, here is my word to the wise: *Just because a company or promotional literature says it, it doesn't mean it's true!* There are many companies in the dietary supplement space that do not have what the bottle says they have. You will spend your hard-earned money on something that will not get you the benefits you are looking for unless you do your homework. So, if you want to get the biggest bang for your buck, take a minute to be sure you know what you are getting.

A delivery system is the way in which a substance is made *bioavailable.* Bioavailability is the extent to which a substance is taken up by a specific tissue or organ after it is administered. In the case of hemp oil, the delivery system is important because the oil is not water soluble and blood is a water-based substance.

Think about making a salad dressing. You typically mix an oil (fat) with an acid, like vinegar or lemon, and some herbs but you have to shake the bottle to get any of the flavor; otherwise you are getting straight oil. If you want to get the oil and vinegar to mix together without having to shake them, you need an *emulsifier,* which binds the oil and vinegar together. For example, you can add mustard or lecithin to emulsify your salad dressing.

Similarly, cannabinoids are *lipophilic* (they bind to fat) which makes them poorly soluble in water. Most lipophilic substances have poor bioavailability so there is usually a higher dosage needed to get the benefits. Hemp cannabinoids are large, fat loving molecules and are not easily absorbed. Blood consists mainly of water, so many processors want to make sure that their cannabinoids are soluble in water and, therefore, also in blood.

Typical CBD oil that is not water soluble still works. I have taken some wonderful hemp oil products that were simply cannabinoids mixed with MCT oil. But, to get a good effect you typically will need to take more. It makes sense that when CBD-rich hemp oil is engineered to be water soluble, the amount of it that can be delivered into the cells is increased. And, when bioavailability is increased, more CBD and terpenes make it through the metabolic process, so you need a smaller amount to get the same result.

For example, if I take 25 mg of tincture that is oil-based I will get about 2-5 mg in my blood. If I eat it, I might only get between 4 and 20 percent bioavailability. So, a person who needs greater amounts of CBD can spend a lot of money getting the dosage they need if it isn't bioavailable.

The question is, which is the best delivery system to get CBD into your cells? That depends on what it is combined with and the target tissue or organ. Research has shown that ingesting pure CBD isolate crystals alone will not get you the results you want, so you want to make CBD without adulterating it or heating it too much. You need the other co-factors, like terpenes, with a good delivery system to get the biggest benefit.

Companies typically sell CBD either mixed with oil, in an alcohol-based tincture, or in vapor form. Tinctures and vaping are absorbed differently in the body than liquids or capsules. Capsules and other liquids contain water-soluble carbohydrates, proteins, and polysaccharides which occur naturally in the cannabis plant but not in CBD hemp oil. So, to improve absorption and deliver a standardized amount of CBD, companies have come up with various unique methods for delivering standardized doses using either liposomes or micelles (explained below).

Sonication

For cannabinoids to be soluble in water, you need an emulsifier, just like you do with salad dressing. Recently, scientists developed a process called sonication that reduces the size of substances like cannabinoids from 2200 nanometers down to as little as 20 nanometers and then emulsifies them to create hydrophilic molecules.

To put this into perspective, a nanometer is one billionth of a meter. Imagine if a regular marble were the size of a nanometer, then a meter would be about the size of the Earth.

Sonication can artificially create *liposomes* (see below) which can encapsulate CBD and make it water soluble. Essentially, a sonicator emulsifies a substance into nano sized particles. Remember, cell walls are very small, so the smaller you can make a particle, the easier it is for that particle to pass through a cell wall.

During sonication, the cannabinoids are broken up at a molecular level and emulsified into a solution. An emulsion is a mixture of one fluid inside a second fluid, like the oil and water mixed in the salad dressing.

Clearly the smaller the particle, the better the absorption. Ultra-fine-sized liposomes, which are 20-30nM on average, begin working within seconds after being dropped into the mouth. Research has shown that nanosized particles can result in as much as 100 percent absorption rate.

This enables you to take a 20mg dose and completely absorb it. This increased bioavailability gives the same results using a much smaller dose, which saves you money.

How Small Is It?

Now that more manufacturers are creating water soluble and nano-enhanced hemp oils, it is important to understand the difference in the size of the particles being created. After all, if you are going to invest in a quality product, you will want to know the size of the particles.

Liposomes

A liposome is a hollow spherical nano-structure inside a cell that has a membrane made up of a phospholipid *bilayer*. (A phospholipid is a type of fat molecule that is the main component of the cell membrane.)

Liposomes are the result of encapsulating lipophilic (fat-loving, like CBD) and hydrophilic (water loving, like blood) substances. They easily bypass the destructive elements in the gastric system and aid the encapsulated nutrients to be delivered to the cells and tissues, which increases bioavailability.

Liposomes work with the phospholipids in the semi-permeable membrane of our body's cells to transport nutrients into the cell. Cell walls are permeable so that nutrients can enter, and waste can exit.

Many nutrients have poor oral bioavailability. So, encapsulating these substances in liposomes is a very effective method for aiding in the delivery of the nutrients to the cells and tissues. Over 50 years ago, researchers discovered that they could fill liposomes with drugs to protect and deliver them into the body and even into specific cells of the body, so this technology is not new, but it is new to the dietary supplement industry and to CBD, in particular.

While the majority of hemp oils that are on the market are liposomal, we may see them in micellized form, as well.

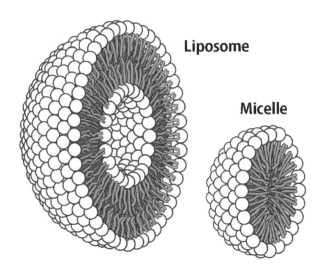

Liposome

Micelle

Micelles

Micelles are nano-sized clusters that improve the surface area for absorption of a substance. In this way, it can reduce the surface tension between two liquids and act as an emulsifier, so this is perfect for oil-based substances like CBD. They are much smaller than liposomes, ranging in size from 2 - 20 nm.

You can learn more about liposomes and micelles at https://biologywise.com/difference-between-micelles-liposomes.

Specialty Products

CBD is now being combined with other nutrients or herbs to make a dietary supplement that provides a specific benefit. Each supplement may use a specific delivery system based on the type of supplement and whether it is made into a pill, a spray, a topical, or a sublingual oil.

Chapter 7
How to Use CBD-Rich Hemp Oil

There are many ways to take CBD hemp oil. It is commonly taken orally in a concentrated paste or in a drops/tincture formula that you put under your tongue. Other oral methods include capsules, mouth strips, chewing gum, sprays, and edibles such as chocolate bars. Many people also use CBD products on their skin via lotions, balms, creams, or patches. Try a few different approaches and see what works for you.

How Much Should I Take?

As much as I would like to have found information giving you the 'correct' answer to this question, I simply can't. The fact remains that everyone is different. The serving size or *dosage (I am not fond of the term dosage because it implies that this is a drug)* will differ for each person, and even vary for the person depending on the state of their health and stress levels that day. Everyone reacts differently to various supplements, too.

Remember that CBD-rich hemp oil products are, by FDA guidelines, *food supplements.* As such, all products are required to have some form of nutritional label on them just like you'd see on food at your grocery store. And, all nutritional labels require a "suggested serving size." But just because this is a requirement, it doesn't mean you have to follow those directions to the tee. You are in charge of noticing how varying amounts work for you. So, work with it to get the right amount of 'food' into your body.

It can be even more confusing because the same product name made by a different company may result in different effects. The combination of terpenes and cannabinoids in a formulation may impact how you experience it. Companies use various source plants, extraction processes, and delivery systems, so one mg. from one product may work like three mg. of another, depending on how bioavailable it is. So, bottom line…experiment and see what works for you.

I suggest that you start small and gradually increase your serving size until you experience the desired result. The first things to consider when determining your needs, are your weight and the severity of your condition.

Try it this way, and see if that works for you:

1. Take 1 serving/dropper full of your daily amount in the morning and 1 serving in the evening.
2. Take it twice per day for the first 3-4 days to build it up in your system.
3. After these first few days, drop back to once per day and see how you feel.

From this point forward, experiment until you feel good. If you do not experience a reduction of the symptoms after 3-4 weeks, you should increase the amount until you experience the desired result. You can also increase the number of times throughout the day that you take it.

Are there any downsides to taking CBD?

While most people will not experience any problems using CBD hemp oil, it can inhibit drug metabolism and the activity of some liver enzymes, such as cytochrome P450.

So, if you are using pharmaceuticals please check with a smart doctor before you decide to mix the two.

How Much is in the Bottle?

Concentrations vary between preparations, ranging from 1 mg per dose to hundreds of milligrams per bottle. This was confusing to me because I was trying to figure out how much I was going to get in a bottle—how many doses and how much per dose. You will see amounts expressed as ml, mg, percentages, and the like. You might see a recommendation of 10 drops as a serving size. And, they might even indicate how many milligrams of CBD are in 10 drops of their product. You will also see that the price goes up as the concentrations get higher.

CBD Hemp Edibles and Capsules

CBD hemp capsules and edibles take longer to take effect than sublinguals because it they are released into bloodstream in the intestines, and so it takes a while before you experience an effect, and the effect is dependent upon the condition of your digestive tract and the bioavailability of the product.

CBD Hemp Topicals

These are commonly used for peripheral aches and pains in the joints or in skin conditions like psoriasis or shingles. Topicals work on the skin and top layers of muscle, so will not work like something you ingest. The topical application of cannabinoids allows them to be absorbed directly for localized relief of pain, soreness, and inflammation. Skin absorbs any lipid-based materials that make contact with it and, therefore, this is one of the most effective ways to ingest cannabinoids. Salves and balms are usually stronger than lotions or creams and all topicals should be rubbed in thoroughly.

Vaporizing CBD

Vaporizing CBD-rich hemp oil is another way to get cannabidiol into your system. It has a fast onset time, so you can determine how much to take more easily. However, the effect does not last as long, so you will need to use it throughout the day. Vaporizing methods are usually not as strong as the straight oils, tinctures, or capsules, and so most people vaporize as an adjunct to their other CBD hemp products.

References for Part 2

1. A Ligresti, et al. *Antitumor activity of plant cannabinoids with emphasis on the effect of cannabidiol on human breast carcinoma.* J Pharmacol Exp Ther.2006.
2. A Pichette, et al., *Composition and Antibacterial Activity of Abies balsamea Essential Oil.* Phytother. Res. 20, 371–373 (2006)
3. Alan Davidson and Tom Jaine, The Oxford Companion to Food. Oxford University Press, 2006.
4. Alice N. Neely and Matthew P. Maley, *Survival of Enterococci and Staphylococci on Hospital Fabrics and Plastic.* J Clin Microbiol. 2000 Feb; 38(2): 724–726.
5. Aidan J. Hampson, Axelrod; Julius, Grimaldi; Maurizio, United States Patent 6,630,507 October 28, 1999.
6. AM Malfait, et al. The nonpsychoactive cannabis constituent cannabidiol is an oral anti-arthritic therapeutic in murine collagen-induced arthritis. Proc Natl Acad Sci USA, 2000 Aug 15;97(17):9561-6.
7. AW Zuardi et al., *Effect of cannabidiol on plasma prolactin, growth hormone, and cortisol in human volunteers.* Brazilian Journal of Medical and Biological Research, vol. 26, no. 2 (February 1993): 213–217.
8. AW Zuardi, Shirakawa I, Finkelfarb E, Karniol IG. *Action of cannabidiol on the anxiety and other effects produced by delta 9-THC in normal subjects.* Psychopharmacology (1982)
9. Bandana Chakravarti, Janani Ravi, and Ramesh K. Ganju, *Cannabinoids as therapeutic agents in cancer: current status and future implications* Current Oncology. 2016 Mar; 23 (Suppl 2): S23–S32.
10. Brenda E. Porter and Catherine Jacobson parent survey of cannabidiol-enriched cannabis use in pediatric treatment-resistant epilepsy Epilepsy Behav. 2013 Dec; 29(3): 574–577.

11. C Guan-Wen, et al., Antibacterial Activity of Emulsified Pomelo (Citrus grandis Osbeck) Peel Oil and Water-Soluble Chitosan on Staphylococcus aureus and Escherichia coli. Molecules. 2018 Apr; 23(4): 840.
12. E Pinto, et. al., Antifungal Activity of Thapsia villosa Essential Oil against Candida, Cryptococcus, Malassezia, Aspergillus and Dermatophyte Species. Molecules. 2017 Oct; 22(10): 1595.
13. EA Carlini et al., *Hypnotic and antiepileptic effects of cannabidiol.* Journal of Clinical Pharmacology, vol. 21, no. S1 (August–September 1981): 417S–427S.
14. EP Baron, et al., Patterns of medicinal cannabis use, strain analysis, and substitution effect among patients with migraine, headache, arthritis, and chronic pain in a medicinal cannabis cohort. J Headache Pain. 2018 May 24;19(1):37.
15. Ethan B Russo *Clinical endocannabinoid deficiency (CECD): can this concept explain therapeutic benefits of cannabis in migraine, fibromyalgia, irritable bowel syndrome and other treatment-resistant conditions?* Neuro Endocrinology Letters [2004, 25(1-2):31-39].
16. Ethan B Russo, *Clinical Endocannabinoid Deficiency Reconsidered: Current Research Supports the Theory in Migraine, Fibromyalgia, Irritable Bowel, and Other Treatment-Resistant Syndromes.* Cannabis and Cannabinoid Research 2016.
17. F M Leweke et al., *Cannabidiol enhances anandamide signaling and alleviates psychotic symptoms of schizophrenia.* (2012) Translational Psychiatry.
18. G Esposito, et al. *Cannabidiol reduces Aβ-induced neuroinflammation and promotes hippocampal neurogenesis through PPARγ involvement.* https://www.ncbi.nlm.nih.gov/pubmed/22163051
19. G. Leson, Pless, P., and Roulac, J. *Hemp Foods and Oils for Health.* (1999) Hemptech,
20. G. Velasco, et al., *Anticancer mechanisms of cannabinoids.* Current Oncology Vol 23 (2016).

21. H Matthys, et al., Efficacy and tolerability of myrtol standardized in acute bronchitis. A multi-centre, randomised, double-blind, placebo-controlled parallel group clinical trial vs. cefuroxime and ambroxol. Arzneimittelforschung. 2000 Aug;50(8):700-11.
22. H Turkez, et al., *Genotoxic and oxidative damage potentials in human lymphocytes after exposure to terpinolene in vitro.* Cytotechnology. 2015 May;67(3):409-18.
23. HS Choi, et al., *Radical-scavenging activities of citrus essential oils and their components: detection using 1,1-diphenyl-2-picrylhydrazyl.* J Agric Food Chem. 2000 Sep;48(9):4156-61
24. *HAI Data and Statistics* | HAI | | MRSA |CDC Oct 25, 2016. https://www.cdc.gov/hai/surveillance/.
25. ID Meng , et al., *An analgesia circuit activated by cannabinoids.* Nature. 1998 Sep 24;395(6700):381-3.
26. IJ McGilveray, *Pharmacokinetics of cannabinoids.* Pain Res Manag. 2005 Autumn;10 Suppl A:15A-22A.
27. J Fernández-Ruiz, et al., *Cannabidiol for neurodegenerative disorders: important new clinical applications for this phytocannabinoid?* Br J Clin Pharmacol. 2013 Feb;75(2):323-33.
28. J Grassmann, et al., *The monoterpene terpinolene from the oil of Pinus mugo L. in concert with alpha-tocopherol and beta-carotene effectively prevents oxidation of LDL.* Phytomedicine. 2005 Jun;12(6-7):416-23.
29. N Okumura, et al., *Terpinolene, a component of herbal sage, downregulates AKT1 expression in K562 cells.* Oncol Lett. 2012 Feb;3(2):321-324.
30. J Wang., et al., *Protective effect of geraniol inhibits inflammatory response, oxidative stress and apoptosis in traumatic injury of the spinal cord through modulation of NF-κB and p38 MAPK.* Exp Ther Med. 2016 Dec; 12(6): 3607–3613

31. JC Chaumeil, Micronization: *A method of improving the bioavailability of poorly soluble drugs.* Exp Clin Pharmacol 1998, 20(3): 211.
32. JD House, et al., *Evaluating the quality of protein from hemp seed (Cannabis sativa L.) products through the use of the protein digestibility-corrected amino acid score method.* J Agric Food Chem.2010 Nov 24;58(22).
33. Jimena Fiz, et al, *Cannabis Use in Patients with Fibromyalgia: Effect on Symptoms Relief and Health-Related Quality of Life.* PLOS.org April 21, 2011.
34. Julia Granowicz, *The Endocannabinoid System: A History of Endocannabinoids and Cannabis.* Mar 13, 2016 https://en.wikipedia.org/wiki/Endocannabinoid_system.
35. Jürg Gertsch, Roger G Pertwee, and Vincenzo Di Marzo, *Phytocannabinoids beyond the Cannabis plant – do they exist?* https://www.ncbi.nlm.nih.gov/pmc/articles/PMC293155 3/.
36. Kerry Bone, Simon Y. Mills, Principles and Practice of Phytotherapy: Modern Herbal Medicine. 2013. Elsevier Ltd Publishers. UK.
37. L. Weiss, et al. *Cannabidiol lowers incidence of diabetes in non-obese diabetic mice.* 2005 Journal of Autoimmunity pp 143-151.
38. LA Parker,et al., *Regulation of nausea and vomiting by cannabinoids.* Br J Pharmacol. 2011 Aug;163(7):1411-22.
39. Linda C. Hodges, et al. *Polysaccharides from Cannabis Sativa Active in Lowering Intraocular Pressure.* Carbohydrate Polymers 5(2):141-154 December 1985
40. *Liposomes.* https://en.wikipedia.org/wiki/Liposome#Dietary and nutritional supplements.
41. M. Bergamaschi, et al. (2011). *Cannabidiol Reduces the Anxiety Induced by Simulated Public Speaking in Treatment-Naive Social Phobia Patients.* Neuropsychopharmacology, 36(6), 1219-1226.

42. M. Friedman, et. al., *Bactericidal activities of plant essential oils and some of their isolated constituents against Campylobacter jejuni, Escherichia coli, Listeria monocytogenes, and Salmonella enterica.* J Food Prot. 2002 Oct;65(10):1545-60.
43. Marie McCormick, et al, *The Health Effects of Cannabis and Cannabinoids.* National Academies Press 2001.
44. Mélissa Prud'homme, et al., *Cannabidiol as an Intervention for Addictive Behaviors: A Systematic Review of the Evidence.* Subst Abuse. 2015; 9: 33–38.
45. *Micelles* https://en.wikipedia.org/wiki/Micelle.
46. N Okumura, et al., *Terpinolene, a component of herbal sage, downregulates AKT1 expression in K562 cells.* Oncol Lett. 2012 Feb;3(2):321-324.
47. Nadia Solowij, et al. *A protocol for the delivery of cannabidiol (CBD) and combined CBD and Δ⁹-tetrahydrocannabinol (THC) by vaporization.* BMC Pharmacol Toxicol. 2014.
48. National Cancer Institute: *Cannabis and Cannabinoids.* https://www.cancer.gov/about-cancer/treatment/cam/hp/cannabis-pdq#section/all.
49. Nora D. Volkow and A. Thomas McLellan, *Opioid Abuse in Chronic Pain: Misconceptions and Mitigation Strategies.* N Engl J Med March 31, 2016
50. Orrin Devinsky, et al., *Efficacy and Safety af Epidiolex (Cannabidiol) in Children and Young Adults with Treatment-Resistant Epilepsy.* American Epilepsy Society. 2014.
51. Paola Massi, et al.*Cannabidiol as potential anticancer drug.* Br J Clin Pharmacol. 2013.
52. Pat Ansen, *Experts Say Epidural Steroid Injections Overused.* Pain News Network, 2015.
53. Patrick Dewals, *Only 13% of Doctors Learn Up to Date Info on Medical Cannabis.* MintPress News. June 21, 2016.

54. Penner EA, et al., *The impact of marijuana use on glucose, insulin, and insulin resistance among US adults*. 2013 Am J Med. Jul;126(7):583-9.
55. Pub Chem, *Geraoniol*. https://pubchem.ncbi.nlm.nih.gov/compound/geraniol
56. R. Adams, Hunt, M., and Clark, J. *Structure of cannabidiol, a product isolated from the marihuana extract of Minnesota wild hemp*. (1940) I. J. Am. Chem. Soc. 62, 196–199.
57. R Mechoulam, Parker, L. A., and Gallily, R. *Cannabidiol: an overview of some pharmacological aspects*. (2002) J. Clin. Pharmacol. 42, 11S–19S.
58. R. Mechoulam, and Shvo, Y. *The structure of cannabidiol*. Tetrahedron (1963).
59. Richard Brotman and Alfred M. Freedman, *Perspectives on Marijuana Research*, prepared for Center for Studies in Substance Use, unpublished, p. 19.
60. Robert Sapolsky, PhD (2008) National Geographic special, *Killer Stress.*
61. Rudolf Brenneisen, *Chemistry and Analysis of Phytocannabinoids and Other Cannabis Constituents*. Marijuana (2007).
62. S. Ross, ElSohly, H., ElKashoury, E., and ElSohly, M. *Fatty acids of cannabis seeds*. Phytochem. Anal. (1996) 7, 279–283.
63. S Uydea, et al., *Enhancement and regulation effect of myrcene on antibody response in immunization with ovalbumin and Ag85B in mice*. Asian Pac J Allergy Immunol. 2016 Dec;34(4):314-323.
64. SC Azad, Rammes G. *Cannabinoids in anaesthesia and pain therapy*. Curr Opin Anaesthesiol. 2005 Aug;18(4):424-7.
65. SC Labs, *Primary Terpenes Found in Cannabis*. https://www.sclabs.com/terpenes/

66. SC Smith, Wagner MS, *Clinical endocannabinoid deficiency (CECD) revisited: can this concept explain the therapeutic benefits of cannabis in migraine, fibromyalgia, irritable bowel syndrome and other treatment-resistant conditions?* Neuro Endocrinology Letters [2014, 35(3):198-201].

67. S Singh, et al., *Fungicidal action of geraniol against Candida albicans is potentiated by abrogated CaCdr1p drug efflux and fluconazole synergism* https://www.ncbi.nlm.nih.gov/pmc/articles/PMC611489 3/

68. Sean D. McAllister, et al. *Cannabidiol as a novel inhibitor of Id-1 gene expression in aggressive breast cancer cells.* Molecular Cancer Therapeutics November 2007.

69. Stanley CP, et al., *Is the cardiovascular system a therapeutic target for cannabidiol?* Br J Clin Pharmacol. 2013 Feb;75(2):313-22.

70. T. Lehmann, Sager, F., and Brenneisen, R. *Excretion of cannabinoids in urine after ingestion of cannabis seed oil.* (1997) J. Anal. Toxicol. 21, 373–375.

71. W Xiong W. *Cannabinoids suppress inflammatory and neuropathic pain by targeting α3 glycine receptors.* J Exp Med. 2012 Jun 4;209(6):1121-34.

72. Yanhua Ren, et al., *Cannabidiol, a nonpsychotropic component of cannabis, inhibits cue-induced heroin-seeking and normalizes discrete mesolimbic neuronal disturbances.* J Neurosci. 2009 Nov 25; 29(47): 14764–14769.

PART THREE
HOW HEMP IS CHANGING THE WORLD

Chapter 8
Hemp for a Healthy Planet

We are at the beginning of an industrial hemp revolution. Over the next few years, we will see an economic boom for hemp businesses in the US, which are not only sustainable but will help clean up the damage done by the petroleum industry.

This chapter discusses the cultivation and uses of industrial hemp and how it impacts the carbon footprint in the environment. Until now, we have been talking about CBD-rich hemp oil and its impact on the human body. So, let's zoom out and look at the body of the planet and discover all the healthy uses for hemp that impacts everything from agriculture to home construction.

On an average day on earth we lose about an acre of rainforest. Every second we lose 72 square miles to encroaching desert. The human population is increasing by 250,000 people each day. Today, we will put 2,700 tons of chlorofluorocarbons and 15 million tons of carbon into the atmosphere.

All of these factors contribute to the ill health of our planet. While environmentalists are making inroads and most governments of the world are waking up, it is challenging for us in the US to make changes that might have short term economic repercussions in favor of a long-term solution.

Typically, we human beings will make those kinds of sacrifices only when the fear of loss is so great that the short-term discomfort is worth the price of freedom and health. You can probably see this in your own life. How often do you make significant changes in your life when the short-term cost is uncomfortable or painful?

It works just like that when we are talking about making a healthy planet with hemp. Those people who have a vested interest in the plastic, petroleum, pharmaceutical, and paper industries do not want change! It is only when the majority of people become aware of the benefits of hemp cultivation and production over that of the current forms of industry, that large scale change will be possible.

What if there were an economical and verifiable method for improving the health of our planet with hemp that could positively impact the personal, environmental, and economic health of our country and the world with an increase in jobs and manufacturing? That might be enough to wake people up. We can do that, and you can be part of it!

Hemp is one of the most versatile plants on earth. It can be used to develop over 25,000 products from nutritional supplements to biofuels to building materials. It could be the answer to untold environmental issues, not to mention world hunger.

Right now, marijuana sales far exceed hemp sales. I believe this is due to several factors, one of which is that people know what marijuana is but not very many people know what hemp is. As we move forward into understanding the benefits of the cultivation of industrial hemp and the manufacturing jobs that can be created, we should see dramatic changes.

How Hemp Can Help the Planet

If you are one of the enlightened ones who believe in science and don't have their head in the sand when it comes to climate change and sustaining our planet, then you will love learning about hemp and what it can do for us.

Hemp and CO2 Levels

Industrial hemp farming reduces our carbon footprint and thereby combats global warming. Global warming has been found to be associated with increasing concentrations of atmospheric greenhouse gases like carbon dioxide (CO_2). According to NASA, **CO_2 levels in the air are at their highest in 650,000 years**. The problem with it is that the CO_2 released from the burning of fossil fuels doesn't get absorbed by most vegetation, so it remains in the atmosphere, causing global temperature to rise.

Industrial hemp uses the sun's energy to convert atmospheric CO_2 into hydrocarbons and water. It acts as a carbon storehouse that absorbs atmospheric CO_2 for as long as the plant continues to exist—even after it has been harvested! This absorbed CO_2 is only released back into the atmosphere when hemp is composted or burned. The wonderful thing about hemp is that as a sustainable crop, it is not composted or burned because every part of the plant is used.

According to a recent press release from *NoCo Hemp Expo*, each ton of hemp removes 1.63 tons of CO_2. As of 2016, the state of Colorado had planted over 8,700 acres of hemp, "resulting in an average of 10 tons per acre of carbon dioxide being removed from our atmosphere." That's 87,000 tons of carbon removed from the atmosphere, and that's just from one state that has only just started cultivating hemp!

Hemp also produces lots of oxygen. Hemp converts CO_2 to oxygen better than trees do. In fact, it produces the same amount of oxygen while it's growing as it would use in carbon dioxide if were to be burned as a fuel.

Hemp and Phyto-remediation

Hemp is one of a few plants that has the property of *phyto-remediation*, which means that it can absorb toxins from the air, water, and soil. It can extract and concentrate certain elements within its ecosystem. For example, it can grow in metal-laden soils, extract certain metals through its root systems, and accumulate them in its tissues without being damaged. In this way, pollutants are either removed from the soil and groundwater or rendered harmless.

Hemp, in addition to brassica (mustard) was planted in Chernobyl, Russia to help detoxify the soil. It is also used to absorb leftover phosphorous on farm land, after the use of poultry fertilizers. While hemp used in this way cannot then be used for food or for medical purposes, it can be used as a construction material or plastic, which is a terrific way to eliminate heavy metals in a safe and healthy manner.

Why Hemp Over Other Materials?

Hemp can be used as a source of food and to make paper, clothing, rope, textiles, biodegradable plastics, and fuel around the world. It can supplant many industrial materials that have been proven to be harmful to the environment because most of these are made from petrochemicals which contribute to planetary pollution and are not biodegradable.

Characteristics of the Industrial Hemp Plant

Industrial hemp is tall and woody, ranging in height from 4 to 15 feet, with a diameter from ¼ inch to ¾ inch. The stem has an outer bark that contains long, tough fibers. Hemp possesses the longest, strongest, and most durable of any of the natural fibers. It produces four times as much fiber per acre as pine trees. Hemp rope, textiles, and clothing are made from these fibers that grow the length of the hemp stalk averaging 8 feet. These primary hemp fibers can be used for composites, reinforcements, and specialty pulp and paper. This fiber is attached to the core of the plant with pectin, a glue-like soluble gelatinous carbohydrate that is used as a dietary supplement and as a food additive, among other things.

The core contains what they call the "hurds" or "shives" (short fibers), which are like hardwood fibers. These fibers are used for building construction and livestock bedding, as well as plastics.

Hemp crops are harvested at various times depending on the product desired. The stalks are harvested for high quality primary fiber as soon as the crop is in flower. Harvesting for seed production occurs 4-6 weeks after flowering, when the male plants begin to shed pollen.

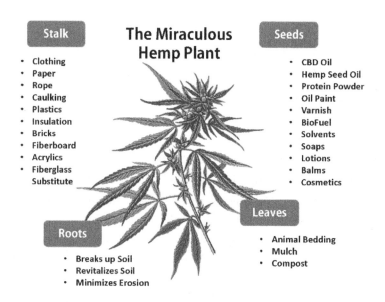

The Miraculous Hemp Plant

Stalk
- Clothing
- Paper
- Rope
- Caulking
- Plastics
- Insulation
- Bricks
- Fiberboard
- Acrylics
- Fiberglass
  Substitute

Seeds
- CBD Oil
- Hemp Seed Oil
- Protein Powder
- Oil Paint
- Varnish
- BioFuel
- Solvents
- Soaps
- Lotions
- Balms
- Cosmetics

Roots
- Breaks up Soil
- Revitalizes Soil
- Minimizes Erosion

Leaves
- Animal Bedding
- Mulch
- Compost

Hemp Cultivation

Industrial hemp grows quickly, so needs little to no pesticides or herbicides. Very few fertilizers are required to cultivate hemp since its leaves fall into the soil and release the required nutrients and minerals, thereby creating a better soil condition.

It is completely sustainable when it is grown in rotation with other crops, like corn or legumes. It is also draught resistant. Erosion of topsoil is limited, thereby reducing water runoff, and protecting this precious resource.

Once the hemp fiber crop is cut, the stalks are left out in the field to loosen the primary hemp fiber from the core fiber. While the stalks lay in the field, most of the nutrients extracted by the plant are returned to the soil as the leaves decompose. The hemp stalks are turned and then baled with existing hay harvesting equipment, using either large round or square balers.

Hemp has a great root structure that returns a lot of organic matter to the topsoil and helps with drainage. After the harvest, the roots remain in the soil, providing nitrogen and other nutrients. This soil makes excellent compost amendments for other plants and hemp cultivation can follow the rotation of agriculture with wheat or soybeans. In fact, the same soil can be used to grow hemp for many years, without losing its high quality.

Once the plant has been harvested, the seeds are taken out and a decordification machine separates the fibers from the wood core. Typically, the seed is used for food and oil, the fiber is used for paper and cloth, as well as raw insulation and door panels, and the woody core can be mixed with lime cement to make hempcrete for construction purposes. Every part of the plant is used, and nothing is wasted.

Paper Production

Paper made from trees requires the use of bleach and other toxic chemicals in the manufacturing process. It tends to yellow with age, and the bleaching process keeps paper white. This contributes to water pollution anywhere paper is made. Hemp can be pulped using fewer chemicals than with wood. Its natural brightness eliminates the need for chlorine bleach, so that no toxic dioxin is dumped into water supply. Instead, hydrogen peroxide can be used with hemp fibers.

Tree Pulp vs Hemp Paper Paper

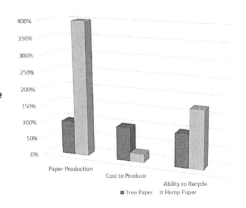

※ Hemp matures in 100-120 days. Trees mature in 50-100 years.

※ One acre of hemp is as profitable as 5 acres of trees.

※ Hemp paper can be recycled up to 7 times. Tree paper can be recycled 4 times.

※ Hemp crops yield up to 10 tons per acre of fiber per year. Trees yield 2.5 tons per acre of pulp per year.

www.HempHealsFoundation.org

Trees used for paper take many years to mature. Hemp for paper takes four months, so you get much greater production from the same land use area. Hemp paper can be recycled up to seven times, whereas pine-pulp based papers can be recycled only three times. It takes just 140 days to be harvested and manufactured into the pulp for paper while timber, by comparison, requires several years before it can go into production.

Clothing & Textiles

Hemp has been used for clothing and textiles for thousands of years. Hemp fibers are longer, stronger, more absorbent and more mildew-resistant than cotton. It was the primary source of canvas, sail, rope, twine, and webbing fiber until nylon was patented in 1937 by DuPont. Hemp clothing keeps you cool on warm days and warm during cold nights. When hemp fiber is blended with wool, cotton, linen, or other fibers, it adds strength, durability, absorbency, and breathability. Fabrics blended with at least one-half hemp will block the sun's UV rays more effectively than other fabrics can. Furthermore, because of hemp's antimildew and antimicrobial properties, it makes more durable sails, tarps, awnings, and floor coverings.

Most of the clothing currently being made is from either synthetic materials that are petroleum based, or cotton. The *Stockholm Environment Institute* (2005) compared the water, land, and energy requirements of cotton, polyester, and hemp textiles. Their findings were interesting:

First, organic methods are responsible for fewer carbon-dioxide emissions than current methods. Cotton uses most of the world's pesticides in its cultivation and hemp requires no pesticides. Polyester takes so much energy to extract the fossil fuel required to make it, it was the most energy consuming of the three.

While cotton requires less energy to grow and process than either hemp or polyester, it needs about twice as much land as hemp per ton of finished textile. Cotton needs about 50 percent more water per season than hemp to grow and more than four times more water to process. Water reserves are well on their way to becoming the most precious commodity on the planet and so this is an important variable.

Most of the fabric made from hemp is currently grown in China and Canada. Wouldn't it be great if it were grown in the USA, too?

Anti-Microbial Properties of Hemp

Many of the compounds in hemp have antibacterial and antifungal properties. This is an important discovery because bacteria on cotton, polyester, and polyethylene remain on surfaces for months at a time. This is particularly pertinent when dealing with healthcare environments. According to the 2014 *HAI Prevalence Survey* from the CDC, there are an estimated 1.7 million infections and 99,000 associated deaths each year, with 72,000 coming from MRSA (an antibiotic resistant strain of staph). In American hospitals alone, by reducing the number of bacteria on surfaces, these infections can be greatly reduced.

While research is just beginning in this area, a recent study was conducted where hemp fabric was tested against staph and pneumonia bacteria strains. The fabric tested was a blend of 60% hemp and 40% rayon. **The staph test sample was already 98.5% bacteria free during the first measurement of the testing, while the pneumonia-infused fabric sample was 65.1% bacteria free.** These results clearly display the fabric's unique ability to kill bacteria and reduce their spread. I would much rather have my hospital bed covered in hemp than cotton. Wouldn't you?

Personal Care Products

Because of the omega rich properties of hemp, it makes a great foundation for personal care products. A *Google* search of 'hemp oil lotion' gave me 850,000 results. I got 1,080,000 results when I searched 'hemp oil soap.'

What accounts for the popularity of these products? Unlike regular soaps, hemp oil soap has extra effective skin soothing properties. It leaves your skin feeling smooth, glowing, and moisturized. CBD-rich hemp oil is added to lotions, lip balms, and creams to provide the pain relief of CBD combined with the skin nurturing ingredients in the hemp. You can buy hand protector, body mist, hair masque, hair gel, hair conditioners, and skin cleansers made from hemp oil. There is clearly a great market for these products.

Biofuel Source

Industrial hemp can be made into ethanol-based biofuels and reduce our dependency on oil and fossil fuels. Hemp falls under a fuel classification known as biomass. Biomass is defined as living or recently dead organisms and any byproducts of those organisms, plant or animal. The energy stored in biomass can be released to produce renewable electricity or heat. Hemp is an ideal source of biomass for fuel. It has four times the biomass and eight times the methanol potential, compared to the current main biomass fuel, which is corn. A single acre of hemp can theoretically produce ten tons—or 1,000 gallons of fuel—per growing season. Hemp produces two types of fuel:

- Hemp biodiesel --- made from the oil of the (pressed) hemp seed.

- Hemp ethanol/methanol --- made from the fermented stalk.

Hemp in Auto Manufacturing

Think back to the turn of the century to the early 1900's. Hemp was still being grown and used for everything from textiles to medicine. That is the era when Henry Ford first built the Model T. The car, 'grown from the soil,' had hemp plastic panels whose impact strength was 10 times stronger than that of steel. The early version of the vehicle ran on both gasoline and hemp-based fuel but as gasoline became less expensive and the prohibition against hemp was building, he phased it out.

Well, if he were alive today, he would be delighted. The technology we have today can make plastics from hemp not only feasible but economically viable. Cars have been traditionally made from steel, which is heavy. It takes more gasoline to move a heavy vehicle and so fiberglass and plastics were developed for use in the auto industry to make lighter cars. However, these composites made from petroleum require a large amount of energy to manufacture.

Natural fibers are increasingly being used in car manufacturing. Because they are lighter, they reduce fuel consumption. German car companies including Mercedes, BMW and Audi Volkswagen have been leading the way in incorporating plant fibers in their models. Since the introduction of jute-based door panels in the Mercedes E class five years ago, German car companies have more than tripled their use of natural fibers to about 15,500 tons in 1999.

Henry Ford wanted to build and fuel cars from farm products. He would be right at home in the educated hemp world of today. He was not in favor of using fossil fuels when making cars, when fuel from farm products worked just as well. He is quoted as saying, *"Why use up the forests which were centuries in the making, and the mines which required ages to lay down, if we can get the equivalent of forest and mineral products in the annual growth of the fields?"*

Plastics

Today we are manufacturing plastics out of hemp fiber as a solution to the non-biodegradable nature of

97

petroleum-based plastic. According to www.statisticsbrain.com, 30 billion plastic bottles made from petroleum were sold in the US in 2016 alone. These bottles wind up in our landfills and oceans where they are polluting our world. They take more than 100 years to barely decompose, releasing toxic gasses in the process. Conversely, hemp plastics are bio-degradable and do not release any harmful substances when they decompose.

Bio-composites made from hemp fiber are just as strong as fiberglass, but much lighter. They cost half of what it takes to make comparable fiberglass or plastics. They take less energy to produce and are a clean resource. Hemp could eventually replace plastics made from petroleum!

Graphene

Waste from the hemp plant can be made into a material that can be used as an inexpensive alternative to *graphene*. Graphene is a nanomaterial used in batteries and high-power super capacitors. It is about 200 times stronger than the strongest steel. It efficiently conducts heat and electricity and is nearly transparent. Graphene is currently being used for super capacitors that include fast-charging batteries in laptops and smartphones, and braking systems in vehicles, including buses and trucks.

Hemp in Building Materials

Hempcrete

Since buildings account for 38% of the total carbon dioxide emissions in the U.S., we should rethink the way they impact the environment. Both the building structures and their interiors have an adverse effect on us and the planet. Indoor levels of pollutants may be 2 to 5 times higher than outdoor levels. Millions of home owners who suffer from *Sick Building Syndrome* are living with headaches, fatigue, asthma, and eye and throat irritation. These reactions are caused by toxic building materials and mold that is trapped in a closed building environment. Homes built with hempcrete, hemp insulation, and hemp textiles can make this a thing of the past.

Hempcrete is a bio-composite material made of the inner woody core of the hemp plant mixed with a limestone-based binder and is used as a material for construction and insulation. The hemp core has a high silica content which allows it to bind well with lime. Hemp is the only natural fiber that has this quality. The result is a lightweight material that weighs about a seventh or an eighth of an equivalent amount of concrete.

Although hempcrete weighs less than concrete, it continues to get stronger over the years. The lime in it turns into limestone, making it incredibly durable and strong. Hempcrete buildings ten stories high have been built in Europe and should last a hundred years or more. The outer walls are made from thick hempcrete which acts as a moisture regulating insulation material, ideal for most climates. They keep the houses cool in the summer and warm in the winter. This saves energy otherwise used for air-conditioning and heating.

Another benefit of using hemp-based construction materials is that as hemp grows, it absorbs CO_2 from the atmosphere and releases oxygen, making it a substance that continuously detoxifies and cleans the air. Think of having walls that breathe as they hold onto toxins and carbon from the atmosphere, keeping them out of the air in the home. Because the walls breathe and regulate moisture, they keep the home mold and mildew free.

Further, hemp is a natural fire retardant. Hemp homes are cost effective to build, much less expensive to run and maintain, have a positive effect on the environment, and create a green, clean, fresh atmosphere to live in.

Hemp Housing Communities

What if you could grow, build, and live in a hemp house all on the same piece of land? They are doing this in the UK right now. Professor Pete Walker, Director of the *BRE Centre for Innovative Construction Materials*, stated, *"Hemp grows really quickly; it only takes the area the size of a rugby pitch to grow enough hemp in three months to build a typical three-bedroom house. Using renewable crops to build houses can also provide economic benefits to rural areas by opening up new agricultural markets. Farmers can grow hemp during the summer as a break crop between their main food crops. It doesn't need much water and can be grown organically."*

Just take a minute and drink this in. Hemp can be used to transform areas that currently have subsistence level housing. Third world areas where people live in conditions where they are not protected from the elements could have affordable housing, a source of food and clothing, and a community that can prosper, all from hemp.

Chapter 9
Hemp Cultivation by Country

Until recently, it was largely illegal to grow commercial hemp in the United States. The US doesn't sit in a vacuum when it comes to hemp use and cultivation. Most of the countries in the world have only allowed hemp cultivation in the last 30 years after having followed the lead of the US for the previous 150. The June 2018 *Congressional Research Service Report on Hemp as an Agricultural Commodity* states that 30 countries across the globe, excluding Canada currently grow industrial hemp. According to the report, "Aggregated production data from the United Nations do not include all countries (most notably Canada) and may differ from other sources but comprise the most readily available source of information. Based on these data, excluding Canada, global acreage in hemp cultivation in 2016—both hemp seed and hemp tow waste—is reported at about 192,000 acres, with a reported total production of 355 million pounds. United Nations data do not include Canada, which is a major hemp producing and exporting country. Including other data for Canada, in 2016, **aggregate acreage totaled at about 225,000 acres**. Canada is also a major supplier of U.S. hemp imports, particularly of hemp-based foods and food ingredients and other related imported products.

This burgeoning crop industry is being discovered as a viable economic solution to problems that plague these countries and it is exciting to watch as people around the world wake up to the value of hemp.

Hemp Cultivation in the US

The 2018 Farm Bill changed federal policy regarding industrial hemp, including the removal of hemp from the Controlled Substances Act and the consideration of hemp as an agricultural product. The bill legalized hemp under certain restrictions and expanded the definition of industrial hemp from the last 2014 Farm Bill.

At least 38 states considered legislation related to industrial hemp in 2018. These bills ranged from clarifying existing laws to establishing new licensing requirements and programs. At least six states – Alaska, Arizona, Kansas, Missouri, New Jersey, and Oklahoma – enacted legislation in 2018 establishing hemp research and industrial hemp pilot programs. Other states are following suit.

You can learn more state statutes regarding hemp at http://www.ncsl.org

States Approved to Cultivate Hemp as of 2018

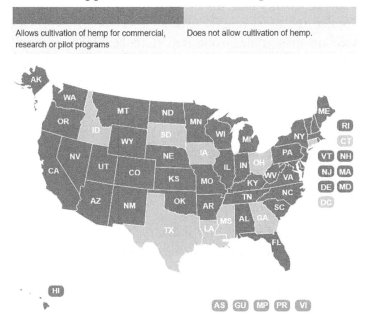

Allows cultivation of hemp for commercial, research or pilot programs

Does not allow cultivation of hemp.

The Top Hemp Producers

China—is one of the largest producing and exporting countries of hemp textiles and related products, as well as a major supplier of these products to the United States. China never banned the production of hemp, even though it restricts the use of marijuana. In fact, because China has allowed hemp for thousands of years, it is no wonder they had secured over half of the 606 hemp patents recorded by the UN's *World Intellectual Property Organization* as of 2014.

- In 2017, Chinese hemp sales totaled $1.1 billion (USD), approaching 1/3 of the $3.1 billion global market, with sales forecasted to grow to $1.5 billion (up 36%) by 2020.

- In 2017, textiles accounted for about 3/4 of China's overall sales of $823 million (USD).

- Hemp-derived CBD accounted for Chinese sales of $53 million (USD) in 2017 but is forecasted to more than quadruple (by 4.3x, to $228 million) by 2020.

Canada—Since legalizing commercial hemp production in 1998, the Canadian hemp industry has continued to expand. The single largest source of U.S. imports of hemp seed and oilcake is Canada. It took advantage of the US hemp prohibition and capitalized on the increasing American demand for hemp products. The Canadian hemp industry was initially centered on hemp production for food but its focus now includes hemp alternatives to fiberglass, textiles, green energy storage, insulation, and construction materials. Canada's Department of Agriculture and Agri-Food has labeled hemp as "the world's premier renewable resource."

Canada encourages hemp cultivation and so the world's largest farmer-owned hemp food manufacturer, *Manitoba Harvest,* flourishes. In the US, *Nutiva* is the number one purchaser of organic hemp in the world today and has a variety of hemp food products. They purchase over 3,000,000 pounds of organic hemp seeds that were grown in Canada each year. The most recent data on hemp production in Canada, from Statistics Canada in 2018, shows there were more than 41,200 acres of hemp grown.

France—Until the mid-1800's, hemp was grown in France to produce fabric, twine, rope, cordage, and seed oil. But, hemp acreage declined and hit a rock bottom of 700 hectares in 1960. Hemp for medicinal purposes was approved in 2013. France is the EU's largest hemp producer and was the third-largest producer of hemp in the world in 2017 with 40,000 acres in cultivation.

Romania—Until 1989, Romania was the fourth largest exporter of hemp worldwide, but the market sank and remained flat until the turn of the millenium. Currently, it accounts for about 70 percent of EU's production. Total acreage in 2017 was 40,000 acres. Some of it is exported to Hungary for processing. They also export to Western Europe and the US.

Hemp Production Across the Globe

North America

Mexico— A bill was signed on June 19, 2017 that officially legalized the cultivation, production, and use of medical cannabis products with less than 1% tetrahydrocannabinol (THC) in Mexico.

Europe

Austria—produces hemp seed oil and medicinals. Although hemp cultivation was never banned outright, interest in farming it declined as global attitudes shifted, and around 1958 the industry died out entirely until the early 1990s. Currently, in line with EU regulations, it is legal to grow hemp varieties containing a maximum of

0.3% THC, for fiber, oil, and all other non-psychoactive uses.

Denmark—began cultivating hemp in 1997 and is committed to using organic methods.

Finland—had a resurgence of hemp cultivation in 1995 with several small test plots.

Germany—In June 2016 through June 2019 Germany has hosted the conference of the *European Industrial Hemp Association*, which is the world's largest industrial hemp conference.

Hungary—is one of the biggest exporters of hemp cordage, rugs, and fabric to the US. They also export hemp seed and hemp paper.

Poland—grows hemp for fabric, cordage, and particle board. They have demonstrated the benefits of using hemp to cleanse soils contaminated by heavy metals.

Spain—grows and exports hemp pulp for paper and produces rope and textiles.

Switzerland—is a producer of hemp.

The Netherlands—conducted a four-year study to evaluate and test hemp for paper and is developing processing equipment. Seed breeders there are developing new strains of low THC varieties.

United Kingdom—lifted their hemp prohibition in 1993. A government grant was given in 1994 to develop new markets for natural fibers. Since then, animal bedding, paper, and textiles have been developed.

South America

Chile—Hemp has been an important industrial plant in Chile since its introduction by the Spanish around 1545. It leads South America in production. Chilean law recognizes the difference between marijuana and hemp and punishes the cultivation of marijuana. There are currently very few hemp farms because synthetic alternatives are more economical, even though synthetic plastics are of inferior quality. There is a concentrated effort for a resurgence in hemp cultivation and new hemp industries are now being developed.

Uruguay—Uruguay became the first country in the world to fully legalize the research and development, as well as cultivation, distribution, sale and consumption of cannabinoids and hemp in December, 2013.

Asia

Japan—has a religious tradition which requires that the Emperor wears hemp garments, so there is a small plot maintained for the imperial family only. They continue to import hemp for cloth and artistic applications.

India—banned hemp cultivation until 1985. The Indian Industrial Hemp Association was formed in 2011 to promote and support hemp industries as a way for Indian farmers and industry to capitalize on the global hemp market.

Australia

Australia—passed industrial hemp legislation in 2017, allowing cultivation after an eighty year ban.

Africa

South Africa—decriminalized all cannabis in 2018.

Egypt, Korea, Portugal, Thailand, and the Ukraine also produce hemp.

Chapter 10
Heal Our Planet with Hemp

I hope I have shown you enough evidence to convince you that cannabis, as industrial hemp, could transform the economy of the United States and any other country that follows suit. The cultivation of hemp is an easy way to make a positive change in our country and on our planet.

To maintain balance, the Earth's resources must be used at a rate at which they can be replenished. Unfortunately, as we have seen in estimates of the rate of climate change, there is now clear scientific evidence that we are living in such an unsustainable fashion we may end up ruining animal and human life as we know it on this planet. Hemp is one of the most simple solutions for creating conditions that can remediate the damage and save this planet. With our economy, environment, and the world's food supply in trouble these days, hemp could be a great solution to many of these problems.

As you have seen, cannabinoids can have a major impact on human health and well-being. We are seeing more and more information on the internet, and hemp companies are popping up everywhere because it works so well for so many things. But there are large numbers of people who do not know what you know right now. I can't tell you the number of times I talk to someone about CBD-rich hemp oil and their mind shifts right away to marijuana. So, we know that many people need to be educated about industrial hemp and CBD hemp oil.

In the fall of 2018, congress federally legalized hemp with the Dec. 12 passage of the 2018 Farm Bill, opening a market estimated to reach $22 billion by 2022.

The Farm Bill removed hemp from the Controlled Substances Act and allows farmers to pursue federal hemp cultivation permits, while individual states can regulate the industry within their borders as they see fit.

According to the *Hemp Business Journal,* the total U.S. hemp industry now looks to expand at a healthy 18.4% through a 5-year combined annual growth rate from 2018-2022. The hemp-derived CBD market will grow from a $390 million-dollar market in 2018, to a $1.3 billion market (3.3x) by 2022, representing a 27.2% 5-year combined annual growth rate.

Further, the passage of the Farm Bill represents a sweeping change in the balance of power in global hemp markets. Until now, the U.S. has lagged behind countries like Canada and France with hemp legislation. The United States has historically imported hemp products from Canada, Europe, and China. Now, the U.S. hemp market will transition to a global exporter of seed, textile, and industrial products and expand to lead the global hemp industry, representing 32% of a 5.7 billion global market by 2020.

We are at the brink of a transformation because of the deregulation of hemp in the US and around the world. But that is just the first step. Each state and local government, as well as the agricultural and housing industries must adopt methods for cultivation and distribution of hemp. Systems for regulation, transportation, and retailing hemp products must be put in place. Advertising and the adoption of hemp as a viable alternative to cloth, paper, food, and housing materials must become commonplace.

Hemp is potentially the richest the cash crop for a farmer, when comparing it to marijuana or corn. Farmers cannot only cultivate it, but they can also process the fiber which, along with sales of the seeds, leaves, and stalks, will render huge profits.

Regulation and management of hemp farms could be relatively easy. For example, GPS co-ordinates could identify hemp farms from the air to compare with any illegal crops, and any hemp crops that are tested to contain over 0.3% THC would be destroyed, as is done in other countries.

The process might look like this:

1. Land is allocated to cultivate hemp.
2. Hemp processing factories are built across the country, adding thousands of jobs in the manufacturing and agriculture sectors.
3. The construction industry manufacturers begin to produce insulation as well as building materials from hempcrete and builders start making hemp-healthy homes across America.
4. Food producers take up the cause and start manufacturing more cereals, flour, and hemp protein products.
5. The awareness of hemp in the use of cosmetics surges.
6. Hemp clothing becomes the norm. You can find it in every clothing store across the country.
7. CBD-rich hemp oil takes the country by storm and people start to feel better and spend less money on medical interventions.

A great way to stay up to date with industrial hemp is to visit www.VoteHemp.com and www.theHIA.org. Vote Hemp was founded in 2000 as a national, single-issue, non-profit advocacy group by members of the hemp industry. Its goal is to remove barriers to industrial hemp farming in the U.S. through education, legislation, and advocacy. The

Hemp Industry Association provides access to hemp producers and advocates in the US and has a terrific newsletter that will keep you updated on changes in the industry.

You can be part of this trend to lead the world in hemp production and use!

The manifestation of this vision depends greatly on you, the consumer. Create a demand for the product and production will follow. Become a consumer of hemp products! Wear hemp clothes. Eat hemp foods. Use CBD-rich hemp oil each day. Every individual who loves hemp needs to select hemp products in the grocery store and ask to have them to be stocked if they aren't already.

We need to ask our building supply stores to provide hemp-sourced insulation for our homes. We need to buy sustainable hemp clothing and paper. As we make these choices and make our voices heard, **the market will drive the need for changed legislation.** As we do these things, we will be healing the planet and its people.

Start today to grow the awareness of hemp. Connect with other environmentally concerned groups and educate them about how the value of hemp will strengthen their cause. Because this plant has been suppressed for so many years, it is amazing how little is known about its tremendous environmental impact. But it's catching on!

What You Can Do

- Post Hemp Facts Through Social Media
- Buy and Use Quality Hemp Products
- Write to Your Legislators about the Benefits of Growing Hemp.
- Arm Yourself with Facts!
- Share This Book!

References for Part 3

1. Amanda Onion, *Hemp Cars Could Be Wave of the Future.* ABC News June 4, 2016.
2. Barbara Filippone, *Lab Testing Reveals EnviroTextile's Hemp Fabric Stops the Spread of Staph Bacteria.* June 2013 PRWeb.
3. Colorado Hemp Company and NoCo Hemp Expo. *Cannabis and Climate Change: How Industrial Hemp Can Help Reduce Our Carbon Footprint.* Loveland, CO -- (ReleaseWire) -- 07/12/2016.
4. Doug Fine. *A tip for American farmers: Grow hemp, make money.* Los Angeles Times, May 8, 2017.
5. H.R. 525 (114th): *Industrial Hemp Farming Act of 2015.* https://www.govtrack.us/congress/bills/114/hr525/summary.
6. Hempcrete 2008 Information Pack. *American Lime Technology.* Retrieved 2010-05-15.
7. Herbert Chase, *Society of Automobile Engineers.* Iron Age Magazine March 30,1941. Cited in the New York Times.
8. *Indoor Air Quality (IAQ)* United States Environmental Protection Agency. https://www.epa.gov/indoor-air-quality-iaq/volatile-organic-compounds-impact-indoor-air-quality
9. Lana D. Harrison, Michael Backenheimer and James A. Inciardi, *Cannabis use in the United States: Implications for policy.* (1995) In: Peter Cohen & Arjan Sas (Eds)(1996), Cannabisbeleid in Duitsland, Frankrijk en de Verenigde Staten. Amsterdam, Centrum voor Drugsonderzoek, Universiteit van Amsterdam. pp. 206-230.

10. Linda Booker and Blaire Johnson, *Bringing It Home*. http://bringingithomemovie.com
11. Mandy Kovacs, *Hemp, Flax Growing as Auto Plastics Building Blocks*. 2016. www.carcam.org/Common/News2/
12. *Market Size: Hemp industry sales grow to $688 Million in 2016*. Hemp Business Journal: State of Hemp 2017 Market Report.
13. Nia Cherrett, John Barrett, Alexandra Clemett, et al. *Ecological Footprint and Water Analysis of Cotton, Hemp and Polyester*. Stockholm Environment Institute, 2005.
14. *OTC Sales by Category 2013-2016*. Consumer Healthcare Products Association. https://www.chpa.org/OTCsCategory.aspx
15. *Profile: Canada's Industrial Hemp Industry*. Agriculture Canada. 2015.
16. Renée Johnson. *Hemp as an Agricultural Commodity*. Congressional Research Service, March 10, 2017.
17. *Sick building syndrome*. Indoor Air Facts No. 4 http://www.epa.gov/iaq/pubs/sbs.html.
18. *Cannabidiol (compound of cannabis.)* World Health Organization Online Q&A. December, 2017. http://www.who.int/features/qa/cannabidiol/en/.
19. *State Industrial Hemp Statutes*. National Conference of State Legislatures. Feb 1, 2019. http://www.ncsl.org/research/agriculture-and-rural-development/state-industrial-hemp-statutes.aspx
20. US Government. *Agricultural Act of 2014*. www.gpo.gov.
21. *World Intellectual Property Indicators*. World Intellectual Property Organization, 2014. www.wipo.int.

Thank you for taking the time to educate yourself about the power of hemp and CBD-rich hemp oil. If you enjoyed my book, it would be greatly appreciated if you left a review so others can receive the same benefits you have. Your review will help me see what is and isn't working so I can better serve you and all my other readers even more. Please go to Amazon.com and click on the reviews.

My vision for us is to live and work together, inspire one another, and integrate who we are as spiritual beings with our skills and talents so that each of us prospers, communicates, and loves with integrity, passion, and compassion.

To learn more about CBD and hemp products, go to www.TheHempMiracle.com. Contact me if you want me to do a workshop or interview with you.

Made in the USA
Middletown, DE
07 April 2019